Name _____ W9-CXQ-413

Date _____ Class _____

Checked by _____

Unit A — Use of Columns in the Standard Form of Two-Column Ledger Account

DIRECTIONS: Each column of the ledger account ruling shown at the right is identified by a capital letter. Answer each item in Part 1 and Part 2 by printing the appropriate capital letter in the Answers column.

ACCOUNT							ACCOUNT NO.
A	B	C	D	E	F	G	H
I	J			K	L		

Part 1: Which letter in the ledger account ruling shows the location for the *heading* titled:

	Answers	For Scoring
0. DATE (debit side).........	A	0. ✓
1. DATE (credit side).........		1.
2. CREDIT (amount).........		2.
3. DEBIT (amount)..........		3.
4. POST. REF. (credit side)....		4.
5. POST. REF. (debit side).....		5.
6. ITEM (credit side).........		6.
7. ITEM (debit side).........		7.

Part 2: Identify the *column* in which the following items are written:

	Answers	For Scoring
8. Year (credit side).........		8.
9. Year (debit side).........		9.
10. Day (debit side)..........		10.
11. Day (credit side)..........		11.
12. Debit amounts..........		12.
13. Credit amounts..........		13.
14. Month (debit side).........		14.
15. Month (credit side).......		15.
16. Word *Balance* (credit side).		16.
17. Word *Balance* (debit side)..		17.

Unit B — Business Vocabulary

DIRECTIONS: Complete each item in Column II by selecting one of the terms given in Column I. Then print the identifying letter in the Answers column. The terms in Column I are arranged in alphabetic order.

Column I	*Column II*	Answers	For Scoring
A — account	0. Because the information recorded in the ledger is secured from the journal, the ledger is also known as a............	E	0. ✓
B — account number	18. The number given to an account to show its location in the ledger is called an......................		18.
C — account title	19. An exchange of property or services is called a............		19.
D — balance sheet	20. An accounting form that is used to sort and summarize the changes caused by business transactions is called an.......		20.
E — book of secondary entry	21. A group of accounts is called a........................		21.
F — business transaction	22. The left-hand side of a two-column account is called the...		22.
G — chart of accounts	23. The right-hand side of a two-column account is called the..		23.
H — credit	24. An entry on the left-hand side of a two-column account is called a.................................		24.
I — crediting	25. An entry on the right-hand side of a two-column account is called a.................................		25.
J — credit side	26. The name given to an account is called the..............		26.
K — debit	27. A list of account titles along with their numbers showing the arrangement of the accounts in the ledger is called a.......		27.
L — debiting			
M — debit side	28. Writing the account title and the account number on the first line of a ledger account form is called..............		28.
N — flow chart			
O — ledger	29. Transferring the entries in a journal to the accounts in a ledger is called.................................		29.
P — opening an account			
Q — opening entry	30. A diagram that shows the sequence of all the steps involved in a particular activity or procedure is called a............		30.
R — posting			

DIRECTIONS: For each of the following items, select the answer that best completes the sentence. Then print in the Answers column at the right the capital letter identifying your choice.

	Answers	For Scoring
0. Writing the title and the number of an account for the first time on a ledger is called **(A)** opening the account **(B)** balancing the account **(C)** posting the account......	*A*	0. ✓
31. The numbering system in the chart of accounts of the Rainbow Car Wash consists of **(A)** two digits **(B)** three digits **(C)** no digits................		31.
32. Each account number is written on a line at the top of the account at the **(A)** left edge **(B)** center **(C)** right edge................		32.
33. In the partial chart of accounts in this chapter, all asset accounts begin with the number **(A)** 1 **(B)** 2 **(C)** 3................		33.
34. In the partial chart of accounts in this chapter, all liability accounts begin with the number **(A)** 1 **(B)** 2 **(C)** 3................		34.
35. In the partial chart of accounts in this chapter, the capital account begins with the number **(A)** 1 **(B)** 2 **(C)** 3................		35.
36. The date of the first entry on the debit side of each ledger account consists of **(A)** the year only **(B)** the month only **(C)** the year, the month, and the day......		36.
37. The date of the first entry on the credit side of each ledger account consists of **(A)** the year only **(B)** the month only **(C)** the year, the month, and the day......		37.
38. In each account affected by the posting of debit entries, the year is written **(A)** on the same line as the account title on the debit side of the account **(B)** on the first line only above the month on the debit side of the account **(C)** on each line on the debit side of the account................		38.
39. The year and the name of the month on the side of the account that is affected are written **(A)** each time an entry is posted **(B)** only once when posting the first entry **(C)** on the last line of the side of the account being used................		39.
40. In posting, the amount *Eighty Dollars* is written **(A)** 80| **(B)** 80|00 **(C)** 80|xx................		40.
41. The number of the journal page from which an entry is posted to the ledger account is written in the account in the **(A)** amount column **(B)** Item column **(C)** Post Ref. column................		41.
42. The account number of the ledger account to which the item was posted is written in the journal in the **(A)** Post Ref. column **(B)** amount column **(C)** Item column................		42.
43. The Post. Ref. column in the journal contains **(A)** dates of posting **(B)** journal page numbers **(C)** ledger account numbers......		43.
44. To distinguish between the beginning amount in an account and the amounts recorded later as a result of normal business operations, the word *Balance* is written **(A)** in the Debit column to indicate the beginning amount or balance of the account **(B)** in the Item column to indicate the beginning amount or balance of the account **(C)** in the Account Title column to indicate the beginning amount or balance of the account................		44.
45. In posting the opening entry to the ledger, the amount in a debit item is **(A)** written last because it is the least important part of the entry **(B)** usually written first because it is the most important part of the entry **(C)** written whenever the accounting clerk chooses to write it................		45.
46. The last step taken when posting from the journal to a ledger account is to write the **(A)** account number in the Post. Ref. column of the journal **(B)** amount in the appropriate column of the account **(C)** journal page number in the appropriate column of the account................		46.

Numbering accounts

Location of the account in the ledger	Account number
1. The third liability account...	*23*
2. The second liability account..	
3. The first asset account...	
4. The eighth asset account..	
5. The capital account..	
6. The fifth asset account...	
7. The fifth liability account..	
8. The first liability account..	
9. The seventh asset account..	
10. The second asset account..	

Indicating to which side of an account an amount in an opening entry is posted   *DRILL 3-D 2, p. 36*

Account Title	Sides of an Account	
	Left-hand side DEBIT SIDE	Right-hand side CREDIT SIDE
1. Cash..	*Balance*	
2. Delivery Equipment..		
3. Pine Street Garage (creditor)...................................		
4. Office Furniture..		
5. John Norman (creditor)...		
6. Daniel Strong, Capital..		
7. Office Machines..		
8. Office Supplies...		
9. Frank Harper (creditor)...		
10. Building...		

Recording and posting the opening entry for a veterinarian   *PROBLEM 3-1, p. 36*

GENERAL JOURNAL   PAGE

	DATE	ACCOUNT TITLE	POST. REF.	DEBIT	CREDIT	
1						1
2						2
3						3
4						4
5						5
6						6
7						7
8						8
9						9
10						10
11						11

LEDGER

ACCOUNT _____ ACCOUNT NO. _____

DATE	ITEM	POST. REF.	DEBIT	DATE	ITEM	POST. REF.	CREDIT

ACCOUNT _____ ACCOUNT NO. _____

DATE	ITEM	POST. REF.	DEBIT	DATE	ITEM	POST. REF.	CREDIT

ACCOUNT _____ ACCOUNT NO. _____

DATE	ITEM	POST. REF.	DEBIT	DATE	ITEM	POST. REF.	CREDIT

ACCOUNT _____ ACCOUNT NO. _____

DATE	ITEM	POST. REF.	DEBIT	DATE	ITEM	POST. REF.	CREDIT

ACCOUNT _____ ACCOUNT NO. _____

DATE	ITEM	POST. REF.	DEBIT	DATE	ITEM	POST. REF.	CREDIT

ACCOUNT _____ ACCOUNT NO. _____

DATE	ITEM	POST. REF.	DEBIT	DATE	ITEM	POST. REF.	CREDIT

LEDGER

ACCOUNT _____ ACCOUNT NO. _____

DATE		ITEM	POST. REF.	DEBIT	DATE		ITEM	POST. REF.	CREDIT

ACCOUNT _____ ACCOUNT NO. _____

DATE		ITEM	POST. REF.	DEBIT	DATE		ITEM	POST. REF.	CREDIT

ACCOUNT _____ ACCOUNT NO. _____

DATE		ITEM	POST. REF.	DEBIT	DATE		ITEM	POST. REF.	CREDIT

Preparing a chart of accounts; recording
and posting an opening entry

MASTERY PROBLEM 3-M, p. 37
[1]

_____
_____
_____
_____
_____
_____
_____
_____
_____
_____
_____
_____
_____
_____

LEDGER

DATE	ITEM	POST. REF.	DEBIT	DATE	ITEM	POST. REF.	CREDIT

ACCOUNT _____   ACCOUNT NO. _____

DATE	ITEM	POST. REF.	DEBIT	DATE	ITEM	POST. REF.	CREDIT

ACCOUNT _____   ACCOUNT NO. _____

DATE	ITEM	POST. REF.	DEBIT	DATE	ITEM	POST. REF.	CREDIT

ACCOUNT _____   ACCOUNT NO. _____

DATE	ITEM	POST. REF.	DEBIT	DATE	ITEM	POST. REF.	CREDIT

ACCOUNT _____   ACCOUNT NO. _____

DATE	ITEM	POST. REF.	DEBIT	DATE	ITEM	POST. REF.	CREDIT

ACCOUNT _____   ACCOUNT NO. _____

DATE	ITEM	POST. REF.	DEBIT	DATE	ITEM	POST. REF.	CREDIT

LEDGER

ACCOUNT _____ ACCOUNT NO. _____

	DATE	ITEM	POST. REF.	DEBIT	DATE	ITEM	POST. REF.	CREDIT	

ACCOUNT _____ ACCOUNT NO. _____

	DATE	ITEM	POST. REF.	DEBIT	DATE	ITEM	POST. REF.	CREDIT	

ACCOUNT _____ ACCOUNT NO. _____

	DATE	ITEM	POST. REF.	DEBIT	DATE	ITEM	POST. REF.	CREDIT	

[3]

GENERAL JOURNAL   PAGE _____

	DATE	ACCOUNT TITLE	POST. REF.	DEBIT	CREDIT	
1						1
2						2
3						3
4						4
5						5
6						6
7						7
8						8
9						9
10						10
11						11
12						12

_____

_____

_____

_____

_____

_____

_____

_____

_____

_____

Recording and posting an opening entry

LEDGER　　　　　　　　　[2, 5]

ACCOUNT _____　　　　ACCOUNT NO. _____

DATE	ITEM	POST. REF.	DEBIT	DATE	ITEM	POST. REF.	CREDIT

ACCOUNT _____　　　　ACCOUNT NO. _____

DATE	ITEM	POST. REF.	DEBIT	DATE	ITEM	POST. REF.	CREDIT

ACCOUNT _____　　　　ACCOUNT NO. _____

DATE	ITEM	POST. REF.	DEBIT	DATE	ITEM	POST. REF.	CREDIT

ACCOUNT _____　　　　ACCOUNT NO. _____

DATE	ITEM	POST. REF.	DEBIT	DATE	ITEM	POST. REF.	CREDIT

LEDGER

ACCOUNT _____ ACCOUNT NO. _____

DATE	ITEM	POST. REF.	DEBIT	DATE	ITEM	POST. REF.	CREDIT

ACCOUNT _____ ACCOUNT NO. _____

DATE	ITEM	POST. REF.	DEBIT	DATE	ITEM	POST. REF.	CREDIT

ACCOUNT _____ ACCOUNT NO. _____

DATE	ITEM	POST. REF.	DEBIT	DATE	ITEM	POST. REF.	CREDIT

ACCOUNT _____ ACCOUNT NO. _____

DATE	ITEM	POST. REF.	DEBIT	DATE	ITEM	POST. REF.	CREDIT

ACCOUNT _____ ACCOUNT NO. _____

DATE	ITEM	POST. REF.	DEBIT	DATE	ITEM	POST. REF.	CREDIT

ACCOUNT _____ ACCOUNT NO. _____

DATE	ITEM	POST. REF.	DEBIT	DATE	ITEM	POST. REF.	CREDIT

[4]

GENERAL JOURNAL

PAGE

	DATE	ACCOUNT TITLE	POST. REF.	DEBIT	CREDIT	
1						1
2						2
3						3
4						4
5						5
6						6
7						7
8						8
9						9
10						10
11						11
12						12
13						13
14						14

Perfect Score..50

Deduct......._

Your Score..._

Name_____

Date_____ Class_____

Checked by_____

STUDY GUIDE

Unit A — Basic Principles of Debit and Credit for Balance Sheet Accounts

DIRECTIONS: Place a check mark in the Answers column to show which word, *Debit* or *Credit*, completes each statement correctly.

		Answers		For Scoring
		Debit	Credit	
0.	The balance of any asset account is always a........................	✓		0. ✓
1.	An increase in the balance of an asset account is recorded as a..............			1.
2.	An entry on the left-hand side of any asset account is recorded as a..........			2.
3.	A decrease in the balance of an asset account is recorded as a...............			3.
4.	An entry on the right-hand side of an asset account is recorded as a..........			4.
5.	The balance of any liability account is always a......................			5.
6.	An increase in the balance of a liability account is recorded as a.............			6.
7.	An entry on the right-hand side of a liability account is recorded as a........			7.
8.	A decrease in the balance of a liability account is recorded as a.............			8.
9.	An entry on the left-hand side of a liability account is recorded as a..........			9.
10.	The balance of the capital account is always a........................			10.
11.	An increase in the balance of the capital account is recorded as a...........			11.
12.	An entry on the right-hand side of the capital account is recorded as a.......			12.
13.	A decrease in the balance of the capital account is recorded as a............			13.
14.	An entry on the left-hand side of the capital account is recorded as a........			14.
15.	An entry on the left-hand side of any account is always a.................			15.
16.	An entry on the right-hand side of any account is always a................			16.

Unit B — Debit and Credit Parts of Transactions Affecting Balance Sheet Accounts

DIRECTIONS: For each of the following transactions, print in the Answers column the capital letters that identify the account to be debited and the account to be credited.

A — Cash
B — Operating Supplies
C — Car Wash Equipment

D — Office Equipment
E — Auto Wash Equipment Company
F — Marco Plumbing Company

G — Harry Shaw, Capital

Transaction	Answers		For Scoring	
	Debit	Credit	Debit	Credit
0-0. Paid cash for new piece of car wash equipment..................	C	A	0. ✓	0. ✓
17-18. Paid cash for a new adding machine.........................			17.	18.
19-20. Received cash from the sale of an old typewriter...............			19.	20.
21-22. Received from Mr. Shaw, the proprietor, a personal check as additional investment in the business..........................			21.	22.
23-24. Paid cash to Marco Plumbing Company in full payment of the amount owed....................................			23.	24.
25-26. Paid cash for operating supplies............................			25.	26.
27-28. Received cash from sale of old adding machine................			27.	28.

DIRECTIONS: For each of the following items, select the answer that best completes the sentence. Then print in the Answers column at the right the capital letter identifying your choice.

	Answers	For Scoring

0. A skeleton form of ledger account that shows only the account title and the debit and credit sides is called
   (A) a standard form of two-column account   (B) a form of balance sheet account
   (C) a T account...

| | C | 0. ✓ |

29. The left-hand side of any account is the
    (A) debit side   (B) credit side   (C) balance side...............................

| | | 29. |

30. Any account balance is decreased by recording an amount on
    (A) the debit side of the account   (B) the credit side of the account
    (C) the side opposite the balance side of the account.............................

| | | 30. |

31. All increases in any account are always recorded on
    (A) the side opposite the balance side   (B) the balance side   (C) the credit side.....

| | | 31. |

32. The difference between the totals of the amounts posted to the two sides of an account is called
    (A) a debit balance   (B) a right-hand balance   (C) an account balance...........

| | | 32. |

33. The debit side of any asset account is the
    (A) balance side   (B) decrease side   (C) right-hand side.........................

| | | 33. |

34. The credit side of any asset account is the
    (A) increase side   (B) left-hand side   (C) side opposite the balance side...........

| | | 34. |

35. The increase side of any asset account is the
    (A) left-hand side   (B) right-hand side   (C) side opposite the balance side.........

| | | 35. |

36. The decrease side of any asset account is the
    (A) debit side   (B) left-hand side   (C) side opposite the balance side.............

| | | 36. |

37. The balance side of any asset account is the
    (A) debit side   (B) credit side   (C) decrease side..............................

| | | 37. |

38. The side opposite the balance side of any asset account is the
    (A) debit side   (B) credit side   (C) increase side..............................

| | | 38. |

39. The debit side of any liability account is the
    (A) balance side   (B) decrease side   (C) right-hand side........................

| | | 39. |

40. The increase side of any liability account is the
    (A) debit side   (B) credit side   (C) side opposite the balance side................

| | | 40. |

41. The decrease side of any liability account is the
    (A) balance side   (B) credit side   (C) side opposite the balance side..............

| | | 41. |

42. The balance side of any liability account is the
    (A) left-hand side   (B) debit side   (C) increase side............................

| | | 42. |

43. The side opposite the balance side of any liability account is the
    (A) debit side   (B) credit side   (C) increase side..............................

| | | 43. |

44. The credit side of any proprietor's capital account is the
    (A) decrease side   (B) increase side   (C) left-hand side.........................

| | | 44. |

45. The balance of any proprietor's capital account normally is recorded on
    (A) the right-hand side of the account as a credit
    (B) the left-hand side of the account as a debit
    (C) on either side of the account depending on the amount of the proprietor's investment....

| | | 45. |

46. The increase side of any proprietor's capital account is the
    (A) balance side   (B) debit side   (C) side opposite the balance side..............

| | | 46. |

47. The decrease side of any proprietor's capital account is the
    (A) balance side   (B) debit side   (C) credit side................................

| | | 47. |

48. The balance side of any proprietor's capital account is the
    (A) debit side   (B) decrease side   (C) right-hand side..........................

| | | 48. |

49. The side opposite the balance side of any proprietor's capital account is the
    (A) credit side   (B) decrease side   (C) increase side............................

| | | 49. |

50. Whenever cash is paid to a creditor, the result causes
    (A) a decrease in capital   (B) a decrease in a liability   (C) an increase in an asset..

| | | 50. |

The effect of business transactions on balance sheet accounts

Trans. No.	ASSETS		LIABILITIES		CAPITAL	
	+	−	−	+	−	+
1.	35.00	35.00				
2.						
3.						
4.						
5.						
6.						
7.						

The sides of balance sheet accounts —
debit, credit, balance, increase and decrease

DRILL 4-D 2, p. 48

Automobile

Debit side
Balance side
+

Credit side
−

Answers to self-checking oral drill on debit and credit

DRILL 4-D 3, p. 48

1. Asset accounts
2. Liability and capital accounts
3. Asset accounts

4. Liability and capital accounts
5. Liability and capital accounts
6. Asset accounts

Analyzing the effect of transactions on accounts

DRILL 4-D 4, p. 49

Trans. No.	(a) Account Titles Affected	(b) Classification of Account	(c) Effect of Transaction on Balance of Account		(d) Recorded on Which Side of the Account?	
			Increase	Decrease	Debit	Credit
1.	Cash	Asset	✓		✓	
	Office Machines	Asset		✓		✓
2.						
3.						
4.						
5.						
6.						
7.						
8.						
9.						
10.						
11.						
12.						
13.						

Chapter 4 ■ 26

Analyzing transactions into their debit and credit parts

1.

Cash
| 25.00 | |

Office Machines
| | 25.00 |

2.

3.

4.

5.

6.

7.

8.

9.

10.

11.

12.

13.

Analyzing transactions into their debit and credit parts

Analyzing transactions in T accounts

Trans. No.	ACCOUNT DEBITED			ACCOUNT CREDITED			DESCRIPTION OF TRANSACTION
	Name	Classification	Effect	Name	Classification	Effect	
1.	Office Furniture	Asset	+	Cash	Asset	−	Bought office furniture for $140.00
2.							
3.							
4.							
5.							
6.							
7.							
8.							
9.							
10.							

Perfect Score..50

Deduct.......—

Your Score...—

Name_____

Date_____ Class_____

Checked by_____

Unit A — Analyzing Revenue Accounts and Expense Accounts

DIRECTIONS: For each of the following items, select the answer that best completes the sentence. Then print in the Answers column at the right the capital letter identifying your choice.

	Answers	For Scoring
0. When the total costs exceed the total revenue, the difference is called **(A)** loss **(B)** revenue **(C)** profit..........................	*A*	0. ✓
1. An increase in capital that results from the operation of a business is called **(A)** a debt **(B)** revenue **(C)** equity......................		1.
2. A decrease in capital that results from the operation of a business is called **(A)** expense **(B)** revenue **(C)** a debt......................		2.
3. Increases in any account are always recorded on its **(A)** debit side **(B)** credit side **(C)** balance side......................		3.
4. The credit side of any revenue account is the **(A)** balance side **(B)** decrease side **(C)** side opposite the balance side...........		4.
5. The balance side of any revenue account is the **(A)** debit side **(B)** decrease side **(C)** increase side......................		5.
6. The increase side of any revenue account is the **(A)** left-hand side **(B)** right-hand side **(C)** side opposite the balance side.........		6.
7. The decrease side of any revenue account is the **(A)** credit side **(B)** right-hand side **(C)** side opposite the balance side...........		7.
8. The side opposite the balance side of any revenue account is **(A)** debit side **(B)** increase side **(C)** right-hand side......................		8.
9. The left-hand side of any revenue account is the **(A)** balance side **(B)** increase side **(C)** side opposite the balance side...........		9.
10. The right-hand side of any revenue account is the **(A)** balance side **(B)** decrease side **(C)** side opposite the balance side...........		10.
11. The debit side of any expense account is the **(A)** balance side **(B)** decrease side **(C)** side opposite the balance side...........		11.
12. The credit side of any expense account is the **(A)** balance side **(B)** left-hand side **(C)** side opposite the balance side...........		12.
13. The balance side of any expense account is the **(A)** credit side **(B)** decrease side **(C)** increase side......................		13.
14. The increase side of any expense account is the **(A)** credit side **(B)** debit side **(C)** side opposite the balance side.................		14.
15. The decrease side of any expense account is the **(A)** balance side **(B)** debit side **(C)** side opposite the balance side..............		15.
16. The side opposite the balance side of any expense account is the **(A)** debit side **(B)** increase side **(C)** right-hand side......................		16.
17. The left-hand side of any expense account is the **(A)** balance side **(B)** credit side **(C)** side opposite the balance side..............		17.
18. The right-hand side of any expense account is the **(A)** balance side **(B)** decrease side **(C)** increase side......................		18.
19. Decreases in any account are always recorded on its **(A)** balance side **(B)** left-hand side **(C)** side opposite the balance side...........		19.
20. Revenue and expense accounts are **(A)** temporary capital accounts **(B)** balance sheet accounts **(C)** not listed on the chart of accounts......................		20.

Unit B — Basic Principles of Debit and Credit for Revenue and Expense Accounts

DIRECTIONS: Place a check mark in the Answers column to show which word, *Debit* or *Credit*, completes each statement correctly.

	Answers		For Scoring
	Debit	Credit	
0. The balance of any revenue account is recorded as a........................		√	0. √
21. An entry on the left-hand side of any revenue account is recorded as a..........			21.
22. An entry on the left-hand side of any expense account is recorded as a.........			22.
23. An entry on the right-hand side of any expense account is recorded as a........			23.
24. An entry on the right-hand side of any revenue account is recorded as a........			24.
25. An increase in the balance of any expense account is recorded as a.............			25.
26. An increase in the balance of any revenue account is recorded as a.............			26.
27. A decrease in the balance of any expense account is recorded as a.............			27.
28. A decrease in the balance of any revenue account is recorded as a.............			28.

Unit C — Debit and Credit Parts of Transactions Affecting Revenue and Expense Accounts

DIRECTIONS: For each of the following transactions of a large automobile car wash, print in the Answers column the capital letters that identify the account to be debited and the account to be credited.

A — Advertising Expense
B — Car Wash Sales
C — Car Wax Sales
D — Cash

E — Electricity Expense
F — Fuel Expense
G — Miscellaneous Expense
H — Rent Expense

I — Repairs Expense
J — Telephone Expense
K — Vacuum Sales
L — Water Expense

	Answers		For Scoring	
	Debit	Credit	Debit	Credit
0-0. Received cash from vacuum sales for the day....................	D	K	0. √	0. √
29-30. Paid cash for newspaper advertising............................			29.	30.
31-32. Received cash from car wash sales for the day...................			31.	32.
33-34. Paid cash for monthly electric bill............................			33.	34.
35-36. Paid cash for fuel oil.......................................			35.	36.
37-38. Paid cash for postage stamps................................			37.	38.
39-40. Received cash from car wax sales for the day..................			39.	40.
41-42. Paid cash for monthly rent.................................			41.	42.
43-44. Paid cash for repairs to car wash machinery...................			43.	44.
45-46. Paid cash for water expense................................			45.	46.
47-48. Paid cash for monthly telephone bill.........................			47.	48.
49-50. Paid cash refund to customer who put two quarters in machine for a car wax job and the machine failed to wax his car..............			49.	50.

The sides of accounts: debit, credit, balance, increase, and decrease

```
                 Cash
Debit side    |  Credit side
Balance side  |
    +         |      −
              |
```

1. Assets and expenses
2. Liabilities, capital, and revenue
3. Assets and expenses
4. Liabilities, capital, and revenue

Analyzing the effect of transactions on accounts

Trans. No.	(a) Account Titles Affected	(b) Classification of Account	(c) Effect of Transaction on Balance of Account		(d) Recorded on Which Side of the Account?	
			Increase	Decrease	Debit	Credit
1.	*Utilities Expense*	*Expense*	✓		✓	
	Cash	*Asset*		✓		✓
2.						
3.						
4.						
5.						
6.						
7.						
8.						
9.						
10.						
11.						
12.						
13.						

Analyzing transactions into their debit and credit parts

1.

Utilities Expense	
18.00	

Cash	
	18.00

2.

3.

4.

5.

6.

7.

8.

9.

10.

11.

12.

13.

Analyzing transactions into their debit and credit parts

Analyzing transactions into their debit and credit parts

Analyzing T accounts

BONUS PROBLEM 5-B, p. 64

| Trans. No. | ACCOUNT DEBITED | | | ACCOUNT CREDITED | | | DESCRIPTION OF TRANSACTION |
	Name	Classification	Effect	Name	Classification	Effect	
1.	Advertising Expense	Expense	+	Cash	Asset	−	Paid cash for advertising expense, $24.00
2.							
3.							
4.							
5.							
6.							
7.							
8.							
9.							
10.							
11.							
12.							

Chapter 5 ▪ 38

Perfect Score..50

Deduct.......—

Your Score...—

Name _____

Date _____ Class _____

Checked by _____

STUDY GUIDE

Unit A — Use of Columns in a Cash Journal

DIRECTIONS: In the form of cash journal illustrated below, each column is labeled with a capital letter. For each of the items listed below the journal, print in the Answers column the capital letter that indicates the column of the cash journal in which the item or the amount of the item should be recorded.

CASH JOURNAL   PAGE

CASH DEBIT	GENERAL DEBIT	DATE		ACCOUNT TITLE	NO.	POST. REF.	GENERAL CREDIT	SALES CREDIT	CASH CREDIT
A	B	C	D	E	F	G	H	I	J

	Answers	For Scoring
0. The year of the first journal entry on this page........................	C	0. √
1. The day of each journal entry on this page.........................		1.
2. The name of the account debited when the amount is not debited to the cash account....		2.
3. The month of the first journal entry on this page.....................		3.
4. The name of the account credited when the amount is not credited to the cash account...		4.
5. A check mark (√) when both amounts of a transaction are recorded in special columns......		5.
6. The source of the journal entry.................................		6.
7. A cash payment...		7.
8. An increase in the balance of the sales account.....................		8.
9. An increase in the balance of an asset account other than cash..........		9.
10. An increase in the balance of an expense account....................		10.
11. A decrease in the balance of an asset account other than cash...........		11.
12. An increase in the capital account as a result of an additional investment by the owner...		12.
13. The check number of a cash payment.............................		13.
14. A cash receipt number..		14.
15. A decrease in the balance of a liability account.....................		15.
16. The amount of a memorandum entry..............................		16.

Unit B — Business Vocabulary

DIRECTIONS: Complete each item in Column II by selecting one of the terms given in Column I. Then print the identifying letter of that term in the Answers Column.

Column I

A — cash journal
B — check
C — double-entry accounting
D — expense
E — footings
F — general journal
G — journalizing
H — memorandum entry
I — posting
J — proving cash
K — receipt
L — revenue
M — special journal
N — T account

Column II	Answers	For Scoring
0. An increase in capital that results from the operation of a business..	L	0. √
17. A written acknowledgment given when something is acquired..		17.
18. An entry to record information that is not to be posted....		18.
19. Analyzing a business transaction into its debit and credit parts and recording each part in a journal...............		19.
20. The recording of the debit part and the credit part of each transaction...		20.
21. A journal that is used to record only one type of entry.....		21.
22. Determining that the amount of cash on hand agrees with the accounting records................................		22.
23. Pencil totals written in small figures.....................		23.
24. An order in writing, signed by the depositor, ordering the bank to pay cash from the depositor's account............		24.
25. A special journal in which all cash transactions and only cash transactions are recorded......................		25.

Unit C — Journalizing Transactions in the Cash Journal

DIRECTIONS: Each column of the cash journal illustrated below is labeled with a capital letter. For each of the following transactions, print in the Answers columns the capital letters that identify the column in which the debit is recorded and the column in which the credit is recorded.

CASH JOURNAL   PAGE

1 CASH DEBIT	2 GENERAL DEBIT	DATE		ACCOUNT TITLE	NO.	POST. REF.	3 GENERAL CREDIT	4 SALES CREDIT	5 CASH CREDIT	
A	B	C	D	E	F	G	H	I	J	1
										2
										3

	Answers		For Scoring	
	Debit	Credit	Debit	Credit
0-0. Paid cash for rent of car wash for month	B	J	0. ✓	0. ✓
26-27. Paid cash for purchase of an asset			26.	27.
28-29. Paid cash for payment of a liability			28.	29.
30-31. Received cash from owner as an additional investment			30.	31.
32-33. Received cash from one day's sales of car washes			32.	33.
34-35. Paid cash for an expense that had been incurred			34.	35.
36-37. Received cash refund for overpayment of an asset that had been purchased			36.	37.
38-39. Paid cash refund to customer because of malfunction of the car wash coin machine			38.	39.
40-41. Paid cash for repair of car wash coin machine			40.	41.
42-43. Received cash from one day's sales of car washes			42.	43.

Unit D — Examining Aspects of the Cash Journal

DIRECTIONS: For each of the following items, select the answer that best completes the sentence. Then print in the Answers column at the right the capital letter identifying your choice.

	Answers	For Scoring
0. The cash journal illustrated in Chapter 6 has (A) one amount column (B) two amount columns (C) five amount columns	C	0.
44. One advantage of using the cash journal is that less time is required for (A) preparing a source document (B) recording a memorandum entry (C) recording cash transactions		44.
45. The first step in proving the accuracy of the entries in the cash journal is to (A) count the cash on hand (B) foot all of the amount columns (C) compare the total of the Cash Dr. column with the total of the Cash Cr. column		45.
46. A check stub is the source document for (A) a cash payment transaction (B) a cash received transaction (C) a memorandum entry		46.
47. A receipt is the source document for (A) a cash payment transaction (B) a cash received transaction (C) the person from whom cash is received		47.
48. A memorandum entry is (A) first analyzed in T accounts before being journalized (B) never journalized (C) never posted		48.
49. A check mark is not placed in the Post Ref. column of a cash journal when (A) a memorandum entry is recorded (B) an expense transaction is journalized (C) both the debit and the credit amounts of a transaction are recorded in special columns .		49.
50. Footings of the cash journal are always made (A) daily (B) weekly (C) at the end of a month		50.

Analyzing transactions that have been journalized

Trans. No.	(a) Account Titles Affected	(b) Classification of Account	(c) Is Account		(d) Effect of Transaction on Balance of Account	
			Debited?	Credited?	Increase	Decrease
1.	Cash	Asset	✓		✓	
	Office Equipment	Asset		✓		✓
2.						
3.						
4.						
5.						
6.						
7.						
8.						
9.						
10.						

Analyzing transactions

Trans. No.	(a) Account Titles Affected	(b) Classification of Account	(c) Is Account		(d) Effect of Transaction on Balance of Account	
			Debited?	Credited?	Increase	Decrease
1.	Cash	Asset	√		√	
	Fees Revenue	Revenue		√	√	
2.						
3.						
4.						
5.						
6.						
7.						
8.						
9.						
10.						
11.						
12.						

Journalizing cash transactions for an architect

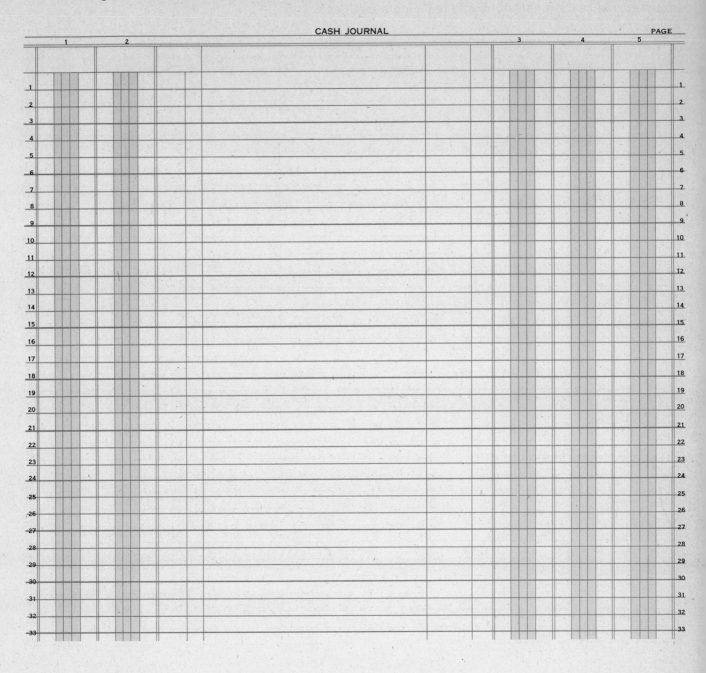

CASH JOURNAL

PAGE

[5] *Prove equality of debits and credits:*

Cash Debit footing.........................$_____

General Debit footing......................._____

Total debits...............................$_____

General Credit footing....................$_____

Fees Revenue Credit footing..............._____

Cash Credit footing......................._____

Total credits.............................$_____

[6] *Prove cash:*

Cash balance, May 1, 19—.................$_____

+ Cash received, May 1–31, 19—..............._____

Total of beginning balance+cash received .$_____

− Cash paid, May 1–31, 19—................._____

Cash on hand, May 31, 19—...............$_____

Problem 6-2 is continued in the next chapter. Your teacher will return it to you before it is needed in Problem 7-1.

PROBLEM 6-2, p. 83

[1-8]

Journalizing cash transactions of a real estate business

CASH JOURNAL   PAGE

		CASH DEBIT	GENERAL DEBIT	DATE	ACCOUNT TITLE	NO.	POST. REF.	GENERAL CREDIT	COMMISSIONS REVENUE CREDIT	CASH CREDIT	
		1	2					3	4	5	
1											1
2											2
3											3
4											4
5											5
6											6
7											7
8											8
9											9
10											10
11											11
12											12
13											13
14											14
15											15
16											16
17											17
18											18
19											19
20											20
21											21
22											22
23											23
24											24
25											25
26											26
27											27
28											28
29											29
30											30
31											31
32											32
33											33

[5] *Proving equality of debits and credits:*

Cash Debit footing.........................$_____

General Debit footing..................... _____

Total debits............................$_____

General Credit footing ....$_____

Commissions Revenue Credit footing...... _____

Cash Credit footing..................... _____

Total credits............................$_____

[6] *Prove cash:*

Cash balance, October 1, 19—............$_____

+ Cash received, October 1–31, 19—......... _____

Total of beginning balance+cash received .$_____

— Cash paid, October 1–31, 19—............. _____

Cash on hand, October 31, 19—..........$_____

Journalizing cash transactions for a taxi business

CASH JOURNAL PAGE

	1 CASH DEBIT	2 GENERAL DEBIT	DATE	ACCOUNT TITLE	NO.	POST. REF.	3 GENERAL CREDIT	4 FARES EARNED CREDIT	5 CASH CREDIT	
1										1
2										2
3										3
4										4
5										5
6										6
7										7
8										8
9										9
10										10
11										11
12										12
13										13
14										14
15										15
16										16
17										17
18										18
19										19
20										20
21										21
22										22
23										23
24										24
25										25
26										26
27										27
28										28
29										29
30										30
31										31
32										32
33										33

[4] *Proving equality of debits and credits:*

Cash Debit footing.........................$————

General Debit footing..................... ————

Total debits............................$————

General Credit footing...................$————

Fares Earned Credit footing.............. ————

Cash Credit footing....................... ————

Total credits...........................$————

[5] *Prove cash:*

Cash balance, February 1, 19—...........$————

+ Cash received, February 1–28, 19—......... ————

Total of beginning balance+cash received .$————

— Cash paid, February 1–28, 19—............ ————

Cash on hand, February 28, 19—..........$————

CASH JOURNAL

PAGE 15

| CASH | | DATE | ACCOUNT TITLE | NO. | POST. REF. | GENERAL | | COMMISSIONS REVENUE CREDIT | |
DEBIT	CREDIT					DEBIT	CREDIT		
									1
									2
									3
									4
									5
									6
									7
									8
									9
									10
									11
									12
									13
									14
									15
									16
									17
									18
									19
									20
									21
									22
									23
									24
									25
									26
									27
									28
									29
									30
									31
									32
									33
									34
									35

[4] *Proving equality of debits and credits:*

Cash Debit footing.........................$_____

General Debit footing...................... _____

Total debits..............................$_____

General Credit footing.....................$_____

Commissions Revenue Credit footing...... _____

Cash Credit footing....................... _____

Total credits.............................$_____

[5] *Prove cash:*

Cash balance, February 1, 19—...........$_____

+ Cash received, February 1–28, 19—......... _____

Total of beginning balance+cash received .$_____

— Cash paid, February 1–28, 19—............ _____

Cash on hand, February 28, 19—..........$_____

Perfect Score..35

Deduct.......—

Your Score...—

Name _____

Date _____ Class _____

Checked by _____

STUDY GUIDE
7

Unit A—Posting the Cash Journal to the Ledger

DIRECTIONS: Illustrated below is a cash journal with its page number and columns color-labeled in capital letters. The posting to the two ledger accounts is indicated by numbers in color. Show the source of each part of the posting as it will appear in the ledger accounts by printing the capital letter in the Answers column. In the first example, 0, the year in the credit entry for Office Equipment, comes from Column D of the cash journal.

CASH JOURNAL — PAGE 1 — A

CASH DEBIT (1)	GENERAL DEBIT (2)	DATE	ACCOUNT TITLE	NO.	POST. REF.	GENERAL CREDIT (3)	SALES CREDIT (4)	CASH CREDIT (5)
		1977 Aug. 1	Balance on hand, $650.00		✓			
1000		1	Office Equipment	R1	14	1000		
	20000	1	Auto Wash Equipment Co.	Ck1	21			20000
B	C	D E	F		G H	I	J	K

ACCOUNT Office Equipment — **ACCOUNT NO.** 14

DATE	ITEM	POST. REF.	DEBIT	DATE	ITEM	POST. REF.	CREDIT
1977 Aug. 1	Balance	J1	50000	0 1 — 2		3	4

ACCOUNT Auto Wash Equipment Co. — **ACCOUNT NO.** 21

DATE	ITEM	POST. REF.	DEBIT	DATE	ITEM	POST. REF.	CREDIT
5 6 — 7		8	9	1977 Aug. 1	Balance	J1	85000

Color Numbers in Ledger Accounts	Answers	For Scoring
0	D	0. ✓
1		1.
2		2.
3		3.
4		4.
5		5.
6		6.
7		7.
8		8.
9		9.

Unit B—Balances of Ledger Accounts

DIRECTIONS: Complete each statement below by circling either the capital letters *DB* (for debit balance) or *CB* (for credit balance). The first item is given as an example.

Statement	Answers	For Scoring
0. The balance of a liability account is always a...............................	DB (CB)	0. ✓
10. The balance of the cash account is always a.................................	DB CB	10.
11. The balance of an asset account is always a.................................	DB CB	11.
12. The balance of the Auto Wash Equipment Company account is always a..........	DB CB	12.
13. The balance of the proprietor's capital account is always a......................	DB CB	13.
14. The balance of a revenue account is always a................................	DB CB	14.
15. The balance of the sales account is always a.................................	DB CB	15.
16. The balance of an expense account is always a...............................	DB CB	16.

Unit C—Basic Principles of Posting

DIRECTIONS: For each of the following items, select the answer that best completes the sentence. Then print in the Answers column at the right the capital letter identifying your choice.

	Answers	For Scoring
0. The memorandum entry on the first line of the cash journal is **(A)** for a business transaction **(B)** posted to the debit side of the cash account **(C)** posted to the credit side of the cash account **(D)** not posted......	*D*	0.
17. The accounting operation that transfers amounts in journals to appropriate accounts in the ledger is a sorting process called **(A)** debiting **(B)** footing **(C)** posting **(D)** journalizing........		17.
18. In this chapter, the first division in the Rainbow Car Wash's ledger is made up of a group of accounts called **(A)** ASSETS **(B)** EXPENSES **(C)** REVENUE **(D)** LIABILITIES.......		18.
19. The group of accounts that makes up the second division in the car wash's ledger is **(A)** ASSETS **(B)** CAPITAL **(C)** EXPENSES **(D)** LIABILITIES.......		19.
20. The third division of the car wash's ledger is made up of a group of accounts called **(A)** CAPITAL **(B)** EXPENSES **(C)** REVENUE **(D)** LIABILITIES.......		20.
21. The group of accounts that makes up the fourth division in the car wash's ledger is **(A)** ASSETS **(B)** CAPITAL **(C)** EXPENSES **(D)** REVENUE.......		21.
22. The fifth division of the car wash's ledger is made up of a group of accounts called **(A)** CAPITAL **(B)** EXPENSES **(C)** REVENUE **(D)** LIABILITIES.......		22.
23. The chart of accounts of the Rainbow Car Wash has a numbering system consisting of **(A)** two digits **(B)** three digits **(C)** four digits **(D)** five digits.......		23.
24. The number *5* in the account number *54* represents the **(A)** maximum number of accounts that can be placed in this ledger division **(B)** number of the ledger division in which this account is located **(C)** position of the account within this ledger division.......		24.
25. The number *4* in the account number *54* represents the **(A)** total number of accounts that are in this ledger division **(B)** position of the account within this ledger division **(C)** number of the ledger division in which this account is located.......		25.
26. When both the debit amount and the credit amount of an entry are recorded in special columns **(A)** both account titles are written in the Account Title column **(B)** a check mark is placed in both the Post. Ref. and the Account Title columns **(C)** each amount in the special columns is posted separately.......		26.
27. In posting an entry from the cash journal to the ledger account, the first step is to write the **(A)** account title **(B)** amount **(C)** date **(D)** journal page number.......		27.
28. The second step in posting an entry from the cash journal to the ledger account is to write the **(A)** account title **(B)** amount **(C)** date **(D)** journal page number.......		28.
29. In posting an entry from the cash journal to the ledger account, the third step is to write the **(A)** account title **(B)** amount **(C)** journal page number **(D)** date.......		29.
30. The last step in posting an entry from the cash journal to the ledger account is to return to the cash journal and write in the Post Ref. column the **(A)** amount **(B)** ledger account number **(C)** date **(D)** journal page number...		30.
31. The amounts recorded in the General columns of the cash journal are usually posted **(A)** every day **(B)** at frequent intervals during the month **(C)** weekly **(D)** yearly...		31.
32. Because the individual amounts that make up the total of a General column are posted separately, the total of each General column is **(A)** frequently posted **(B)** not posted **(C)** posted weekly **(D)** posted monthly......		32.
33. Each time an individual amount in a General column is posted, the number of the account to which it is posted is recorded in the **(A)** Post. Ref. column of the journal **(B)** No. column of the journal **(C)** Account Title column of the journal.......		33.
34. A check mark in parentheses ($\sqrt{}$) is placed under the total of a General column to show that the total of a column is **(A)** posted **(B)** equal **(C)** in balance **(D)** not posted.......		34.
35. The account number is placed in parentheses under the total of a special column to show **(A)** to which account the total eventually will be posted **(B)** to which account the total has been posted **(C)** that the totals of the columns have been proved.......		35.

Reviewing account numbers

Location of the account in the ledger	Account Number	Location of the account in the ledger	Account Number
1. The second liability account......	22	7. The capital account.............	_____
2. The second revenue account......	_____	8. The seventh asset account........	_____
3. The third liability account.......	_____	9. The seventh expense account......	_____
4. The third asset account..........	_____	10. The sixth expense account........	_____
5. The first expense account........	_____	11. The sixth liability account........	_____
6. The first revenue account........	_____	12. The fourth expense account.......	_____

Analyzing the cash journal after posting   *DRILL 7-D 2, p. 101*

1. _____

2. _____

3. _____

   _____

4. _____

5. _____

6. _____

7. _____

8. _____

9. _____

Analyzing the ledger   *Drill 7-D 3, p. 101*

1. _____

2. _____

3. _____

4. _____

5. _____

   _____

   _____

   _____

   _____

6. _____

LEDGER

ACCOUNT *Cash* ACCOUNT NO. *11*

DATE	ITEM	POST. REF.	DEBIT	DATE	ITEM	POST. REF.	CREDIT
Oct. 1	Balance	✓	86050				

ACCOUNT *Automobile* ACCOUNT NO. *12*

DATE	ITEM	POST. REF.	DEBIT	DATE	ITEM	POST. REF.	CREDIT
Oct. 1	Balance	✓	175000				

ACCOUNT *Office Furniture* ACCOUNT NO. *13*

DATE	ITEM	POST. REF.	DEBIT	DATE	ITEM	POST. REF.	CREDIT
Oct. 1	Balance	✓	76000				

ACCOUNT *Office Machines* ACCOUNT NO. *14*

DATE	ITEM	POST. REF.	DEBIT	DATE	ITEM	POST. REF.	CREDIT
Oct. 1	Balance	✓	55000				

ACCOUNT *Hadley Company* ACCOUNT NO. *21*

DATE	ITEM	POST. REF.	DEBIT	DATE	ITEM	POST. REF.	CREDIT
				Oct. 1	Balance	✓	18500

ACCOUNT *Rick's Garage* ACCOUNT NO. *22*

DATE	ITEM	POST. REF.	DEBIT	DATE	ITEM	POST. REF.	CREDIT
				Oct. 1	Balance	✓	9250

LEDGER

ACCOUNT *Hiram Sims, Capital*   ACCOUNT NO. 31

DATE	ITEM	POST. REF.	DEBIT	DATE	ITEM	POST. REF.	CREDIT
				Oct. 1	Balance	✓	364300

ACCOUNT *Commissions Revenue*   ACCOUNT NO. 41

DATE	ITEM	POST. REF.	DEBIT	DATE	ITEM	POST. REF.	CREDIT

ACCOUNT *Advertising Expense*   ACCOUNT NO. 51

DATE	ITEM	POST. REF.	DEBIT	DATE	ITEM	POST. REF.	CREDIT

ACCOUNT *Automobile Expense*   ACCOUNT NO. 52

DATE	ITEM	POST. REF.	DEBIT	DATE	ITEM	POST. REF.	CREDIT

ACCOUNT *Miscellaneous Expense*   ACCOUNT NO. 53

DATE	ITEM	POST. REF.	DEBIT	DATE	ITEM	POST. REF.	CREDIT

ACCOUNT *Rent Expense*   ACCOUNT NO. 54

DATE	ITEM	POST. REF.	DEBIT	DATE	ITEM	POST. REF.	CREDIT

CASH JOURNAL

PAGE

	1	2					3	4	5	
	CASH DEBIT	GENERAL DEBIT	DATE	ACCOUNT TITLE	NO.	POST. REF.	GENERAL CREDIT	ADMISSIONS REVENUE CREDIT	CASH CREDIT	
1										1
2										2
3										3
4										4
5										5
6										6
7										7
8										8
9										9
10										10
11										11
12										12
13										13
14										14
15										15
16										16
17										17
18										18
19										19
20										20
21										21
22										22
23										23
24										24
25										25
26										26
27										27
28										28
29										29
30										30
31										31
32										32
33										33

[6] *Proving equality of debits and credits:*

Cash Debit footing.......................$_____

General Debit footing....................._____

Total debits.............................$_____

General Credit footing...................$_____

Admissions Revenue Credit footing......._____

Cash Credit footing......................._____

Total credits............................$_____

[7] *Prove cash:*

Cash balance, July 1, 19—................$_____

+ Cash received, July 1–31, 19—............._____

Total of beginning balance+cash received .$_____

− Cash paid, July 1–31, 19—................_____

Cash on hand, July 31, 19—..............$_____

LEDGER

ACCOUNT _____ ACCOUNT NO. _____

DATE	ITEM	POST. REF.	DEBIT	DATE	ITEM	POST. REF.	CREDIT

ACCOUNT _____ ACCOUNT NO. _____

DATE	ITEM	POST. REF.	DEBIT	DATE	ITEM	POST. REF.	CREDIT

ACCOUNT _____ ACCOUNT NO. _____

DATE	ITEM	POST. REF.	DEBIT	DATE	ITEM	POST. REF.	CREDIT

ACCOUNT _____ ACCOUNT NO. _____

DATE	ITEM	POST. REF.	DEBIT	DATE	ITEM	POST. REF.	CREDIT

ACCOUNT _____ ACCOUNT NO. _____

DATE	ITEM	POST. REF.	DEBIT	DATE	ITEM	POST. REF.	CREDIT

ACCOUNT _____ ACCOUNT NO. _____

DATE	ITEM	POST. REF.	DEBIT	DATE	ITEM	POST. REF.	CREDIT

LEDGER

ACCOUNT _____   ACCOUNT NO. _____

	DATE	ITEM	POST. REF.	DEBIT	DATE	ITEM	POST. REF.	CREDIT	

ACCOUNT _____   ACCOUNT NO. _____

	DATE	ITEM	POST. REF.	DEBIT	DATE	ITEM	POST. REF.	CREDIT	

ACCOUNT _____   ACCOUNT NO. _____

	DATE	ITEM	POST. REF.	DEBIT	DATE	ITEM	POST. REF.	CREDIT	

ACCOUNT _____   ACCOUNT NO. _____

	DATE	ITEM	POST. REF.	DEBIT	DATE	ITEM	POST. REF.	CREDIT	

ACCOUNT _____   ACCOUNT NO. _____

	DATE	ITEM	POST. REF.	DEBIT	DATE	ITEM	POST. REF.	CREDIT	

ACCOUNT _____   ACCOUNT NO. _____

	DATE	ITEM	POST. REF.	DEBIT	DATE	ITEM	POST. REF.	CREDIT	

[3-10]

Journalizing and posting the transactions of a psychiatrist's office

CASH JOURNAL

PAGE

| | CASH | | DATE | ACCOUNT TITLE | NO. | POST. REF. | GENERAL | | PROFESSIONAL FEES CREDIT | |
	DEBIT	CREDIT					DEBIT	CREDIT		
1										1
2										2
3										3
4										4
5										5
6										6
7										7
8										8
9										9
10										10
11										11
12										12
13										13
14										14
15										15
16										16
17										17
18										18
19										19
20										20
21										21
22										22
23										23
24										24
25										25
26										26
27										27
28										28
29										29
30										30
31										31
32										32
33										33
34										34
35										35

[6] *Proving equality of debits and credits:*

Cash Debit footing.........................$_____

General Debit footing..................... _____

Total debits..............................$_____

General Credit footing....................$_____

Professional Fees Credit footing.......... _____

Cash Credit footing....................... _____

Total credits.............................$_____

[7] *Prove cash:*

Cash balance, August 1, 19—..............$_____

+ Cash received, August 1–31, 19—.......... _____

Total of beginning balance+cash received .$_____

− Cash paid, August 1-31, 19—............. _____

Cash on hand, August 31, 19—............$_____

LEDGER

ACCOUNT _____ ACCOUNT NO. _____

DATE	ITEM	POST. REF.	DEBIT	DATE	ITEM	POST. REF.	CREDIT

ACCOUNT _____ ACCOUNT NO. _____

DATE	ITEM	POST. REF.	DEBIT	DATE	ITEM	POST. REF.	CREDIT

ACCOUNT _____ ACCOUNT NO. _____

DATE	ITEM	POST. REF.	DEBIT	DATE	ITEM	POST. REF.	CREDIT

ACCOUNT _____ ACCOUNT NO. _____

DATE	ITEM	POST. REF.	DEBIT	DATE	ITEM	POST. REF.	CREDIT

LEDGER

ACCOUNT _____ ACCOUNT NO. _____

DATE		ITEM	POST. REF.	DEBIT	DATE		ITEM	POST. REF.	CREDIT

ACCOUNT _____ ACCOUNT NO. _____

DATE		ITEM	POST. REF.	DEBIT	DATE		ITEM	POST. REF.	CREDIT

ACCOUNT _____ ACCOUNT NO. _____

DATE		ITEM	POST. REF.	DEBIT	DATE		ITEM	POST. REF.	CREDIT

ACCOUNT _____ ACCOUNT NO. _____

DATE		ITEM	POST. REF.	DEBIT	DATE		ITEM	POST. REF.	CREDIT

LEDGER

ACCOUNT _____ ACCOUNT NO. _____

DATE	ITEM	POST. REF.	DEBIT	DATE	ITEM	POST. REF.	CREDIT

ACCOUNT _____ ACCOUNT NO. _____

DATE	ITEM	POST. REF.	DEBIT	DATE	ITEM	POST. REF.	CREDIT

ACCOUNT _____ ACCOUNT NO. _____

DATE	ITEM	POST. REF.	DEBIT	DATE	ITEM	POST. REF.	CREDIT

ACCOUNT _____ ACCOUNT NO. _____

DATE	ITEM	POST. REF.	DEBIT	DATE	ITEM	POST. REF.	CREDIT

Perfect Score..35

Deduct.......

Your Score...

Name _____

Date _____ Class _____

Checked by _____

Unit A—Footing and Recording the Balances of Ledger Accounts

DIRECTIONS: Each column of the ledger account illustrated at the right is labeled with a capital letter. For each of the following items, print in the Answers column the capital letter identifying the column in which the *amount* is found after the ledger account has been footed and the balance figured and recorded.

ACCOUNT									ACCOUNT NO.	
DATE	ITEM	POST. REF.	DEBIT	DATE	ITEM	POST. REF.	CREDIT			
A	B	C	D	E	F	G	H	I	J	

	Answers	For Scoring
0. Amount of a debit pencil footing..	E	0. ✓
1. Amount of a credit pencil footing.......................................		1.
2. Amount of the balance in the operating supplies account, *(entries on one side only)*.........		2.
3. Amount of the balance in the cash account.............................		3.
4. Amount of the balance in the creditor's account, Marco Plumbing Company *(only one entry)*......		4.
5. Amount of the balance in the office equipment account *(one debit and two credit entries)*.....		5.
6. Amount of the balance in the car wash equipment account *(only one entry)*...............		6.
7. Amount of the balance in the creditor's account, Auto Wash Equipment Company *(only one entry on each side)*.........		7.
8. Amount of the balance in the sales account *(only one entry)*....................		8.
9. Amount of the balance in the Harry Shaw Capital account *(entries on one side only)*........		9.
10. Amount of the balance in the miscellaneous expense account *(several entries, all on one side)*..		10.
11. Amount of the balance in the rent expense account *(only one entry)*....................		11.
12. Amount of the balance in the utilities expense account *(several entries, all on one side)*........		12.

Unit B—Locating Data on a Trial Balance

DIRECTIONS: Decide in which of the places on a trial balance each is written. Then write the capital letter from the illustration identifying your choice.

A
B
C

D E   F   G   H

	Answers	For Scoring
0. Day for which trial balance is prepared.........	C	0. ✓
13. Name of the business.....		13.
14. Debit account balances...		14.
15. Words *Trial Balance*......		15.
16. Month which trial balance is prepared...........		16.
17. Ledger account numbers..		17.
18. Account titles...........		18.
19. Credit account balances..		19.
20. Year in which trial balance is prepared.........		20.

DIRECTIONS: For each of the following items, select the answer that best completes the sentence. Then print in the Answers column at the right the capital letter identifying your choice.

	Answers	For Scoring

0. The balance of the cash account is found by
   (A) comparing cash on hand with cash in the bank
   (B) finding the difference between the totals of the two sides of the account
   (C) comparing the check book balance with the cash account balance...................

   B   0. ✓

21. The first step in determining and recording the balance of the cash account is to
    (A) compare the amount of cash on hand with the account balance   (B) figure the account balance   (C) foot the columns   (D) record the account balance..........

    21.

22. The second step in figuring and recording the balance of the cash account is to
    (A) compare the amount of cash on hand with the account balance   (B) figure the account balance   (C) foot the columns   (D) record the account balance............

    22.

23. The third step in determining and recording the balance of the cash account is to
    (A) compare the amount of cash on hand with the account balance   (B) figure the account balance   (C) foot the columns   (D) record the account balance..........

    23.

24. The cash account is said to be proved when the cash on hand and in the bank is found to agree with the balance
    (A) of the cash account   (B) in the proprietor's capital account   (C) of all asset accounts..

    24.

25. The pencil footing on the debit side of an account is written
    (A) immediately under the last amount in the Debit column   (B) in the Item column on the debit side   (C) on the next line below the last debit amount.................

    25.

26. A ledger account with several entries on each side has its balance written
    (A) on both sides of the account   (B) in the Item column on the side that has the larger footing   (C) on the side that has the smaller footing..............................

    26.

27. A ledger account with two or more entries on one side only has
    (A) its balance written in the Item column on the side that has the entries
    (B) its balance written in the Item column on the side without entries
    (C) the footing as its balance.........

    27.

28. A ledger account with only one debit entry and one credit entry has its balance written in the Item column on
    (A) the side that has the smaller amount   (B) the side that has the larger amount
    (C) neither side.........

    28.

29. The proof of the equality of the debits and the credits in the ledger is called a
    (A) balance sheet   (B) journal   (C) ledger   (D) trial balance.................

    29.

30. A trial balance that is in balance
    (A) always proves the accuracy of journalizing   (B) always proves the accuracy of posting   (C) does not always prove the complete accuracy of the records............

    30.

31. When an amount is posted to the correct side of an account, but to the wrong account, the trial balance will
    (A) disclose the error   (B) still be in balance   (C) not be in balance..............

    31.

32. If the journalizing of a transaction is omitted
    (A) the ledger will not be in balance   (B) the error will be indicated by the trial balance
    (C) the error will not be indicated by the trial balance......................

    32.

33. When a trial balance fails to balance, the first thing recommended to do is
    (A) look for the error in the journal   (B) look for the error in the ledger
    (C) re-add the trial balance columns......................................

    33.

34. When the correct amount is $12.43 and an accountant makes the mistake of writing it as $14.23 or $21.43 or $12.34, the kind of error he has committed is called a
    (A) composition   (B) transposition   (C) slide.....................

    34.

35. An error in a pencil footing in the ledger should
    (A) be replaced by an ink footing   (B) be erased and replaced by the correct pencil footing   (C) have a line drawn through it and the correct footing written underneath....

    35.

Analyzing the ledger

1. _____

2. _____

3. _____

_____

_____

_____

Classifying accounts and entering their balances on a trial balance

Account Title	Classifi-cation	Trial Balance	
		Debit	Credit
1. Advertising Expense..............................	E	60.00	
2.			
3.			
4.			
5.			
6.			
7.			
8.			
9.			
10.			
11.			
12.			
13.			
14.			

LEDGER

ACCOUNT *Cash*   ACCOUNT NO. 11

DATE		ITEM	POST. REF.	DEBIT	DATE		ITEM	POST. REF.	CREDIT
19-- Oct.	1	Balance	J1	2411 97	19-- Oct.	31		C2	1355 20
	31		C2	1142 60					

ACCOUNT *Automobile*   ACCOUNT NO. 12

DATE		ITEM	POST. REF.	DEBIT	DATE	ITEM	POST. REF.	CREDIT
19-- Oct.	1	Balance	J1	2970 00				

ACCOUNT *Office Equipment*   ACCOUNT NO. 13

DATE		ITEM	POST. REF.	DEBIT	DATE	ITEM	POST. REF.	CREDIT
19-- Oct.	1	Balance	J1	1172 10				
	5		C1	60 00				
	25		C2	65 21				

ACCOUNT *Office Furniture*   ACCOUNT NO. 14

DATE		ITEM	POST. REF.	DEBIT	DATE		ITEM	POST. REF.	CREDIT
19-- Oct.	1	Balance	J1	550 00	19-- Oct.	16		C1	45 00
	22		C1	75 00					

ACCOUNT *Jackson and King*   ACCOUNT NO. 21

DATE		ITEM	POST. REF.	DEBIT	DATE		ITEM	POST. REF.	CREDIT
19-- Oct.	17		C1	126 14	19-- Oct.	1	Balance	J1	856 14
	22		C1	100 00					

LEDGER

ACCOUNT _Martin Company_   ACCOUNT NO. 22

DATE	ITEM	POST. REF.	DEBIT	DATE	ITEM	POST. REF.	CREDIT
19-- Oct. 12		C1	17500	19-- Oct. 1	Balance	J1	36048
25		C1	10000				

ACCOUNT _Elouise Garrison, Capital_   ACCOUNT NO. 31

DATE	ITEM	POST. REF.	DEBIT	DATE	ITEM	POST. REF.	CREDIT
				19-- Oct. 1	Balance	J1	588745

ACCOUNT _Commissions Revenue_   ACCOUNT NO. 41

DATE	ITEM	POST. REF.	DEBIT	DATE	ITEM	POST. REF.	CREDIT
				19-- Oct. 31		C2	109760

ACCOUNT _Advertising Expense_   ACCOUNT NO. 51

DATE	ITEM	POST. REF.	DEBIT	DATE	ITEM	POST. REF.	CREDIT
19-- Oct. 12		C1	4569				
29		C2	20740				

ACCOUNT _Automobile Expense_   ACCOUNT NO. 52

DATE	ITEM	POST. REF.	DEBIT	DATE	ITEM	POST. REF.	CREDIT
19-- Oct. 15		C1	2656				
31		C2	18235				

ACCOUNT _Miscellaneous Expense_   ACCOUNT NO. 53

DATE	ITEM	POST. REF.	DEBIT	DATE	ITEM	POST. REF.	CREDIT
19-- Oct. 16		C1	1764				
31		C2	3681				

LEDGER

ACCOUNT *Rent Expense*   ACCOUNT NO. 54

DATE	ITEM	POST. REF.	DEBIT	DATE	ITEM	POST. REF.	CREDIT
19-- Oct. 31		C2	12500				

ACCOUNT *Stationery Expense*   ACCOUNT NO. 55

DATE	ITEM	POST. REF.	DEBIT	DATE	ITEM	POST. REF.	CREDIT
19-- Oct. 3		C1	310				
26		C2	930				

[3]

ACCOUNT TITLE	ACCT. NO.	DEBIT	CREDIT

Finding and correcting errors indicated by a trial balance

[3]

Prepare the trial balance for Instruction 3 of Problem 8-2 on page 68 of this workbook. Use the cash journal illustrated below only if an error or errors are disclosed by this trial balance.

CASH JOURNAL

PAGE 2

	CASH DEBIT	GENERAL DEBIT	DATE	ACCOUNT TITLE	NO.	POST. REF.	GENERAL CREDIT	FEES REVENUE CREDIT	CASH CREDIT	
1			19— Nov. 1	Balance on hand, $785.00		✓				1
2		17500	1	Rent Expense	Ck1	53			17500	2
3		5037	4	Supplies Expense	Ck2	54			5037	3
4	6550		7	✓	R1	✓		6550		4
5		7975	7	Martin Supplies, Inc.	Ck3	21			7975	5
6		2130	9	Miscellaneous Expense	Ck4	52			2130	6
7	13250		10	✓	R2	✓		13250		7
8		4500	11	Office Furniture	Ck5	13			4500	8
9		1439	11	Automobile Expense	Ck6	51			1439	9
10		8426	14	Supplies Expense	Ck7	54			8426	10
11	26000		14	✓	R3	✓		26000		11
12		915	16	Miscellaneous Expense	Ck8	52			915	12
13		1349	16	Automobile Expense	Ck9	51			1349	13
14	9300		18	✓	R4	✓		9300		14
15	34250		21	✓	R5	✓		34250		15
16		3314	21	Supplies Expense	Ck10	54			3314	16
17		5180	22	Miscellaneous Expense	Ck11	52			5180	17
18	17700		23	✓	R6	✓		17700		18
19		1350	24	Automobile Expense	Ck12	51			1350	19
20		21545	25	Wilson Company	Ck13	23			21545	20
21	3500		25	Office Furniture	R7	13	3500			21
22	21000		28	✓	R8	✓		21000		22
23		10000	28	Samson Company	Ck14	22			10000	23
24		1260	29	Automobile Expense	Ck15	51			1260	24
25		1625	29	Miscellaneous Expense	Ck16	52			1625	25
26	4500		29	✓	R9	✓		4500		26
27		1030	30	Telephone Expense	Ck17	55			1030	27
28		1238	30	Miscellaneous Expense	Ck18	52			1238	28
29		37000	30	Office Equipment	Ck19	14			37000	29
30	27500		30	✓	R10	✓		27500		30
31										31
32										32
33										33
34										34
35										35
36										36
37										37
38										38
39										39
40										40
41										41
42										42
43										43
44	163550	132813					3500	160050	132813	44
45	163550	132813	30	Totals			3500	160050	132813	45
	(11)	(✓)					(✓)	(41)	(11)	

LEDGER

ACCOUNT **Cash** — ACCOUNT NO. **11**

DATE		ITEM	POST. REF.	DEBIT	DATE		ITEM	POST. REF.	CREDIT
19-- Nov.	1	Balance	J1	785 00	19-- Nov.	30		C2	1 328 13
	30		C2	1 635 50					

ACCOUNT **Automobile** — ACCOUNT NO. **12**

DATE		ITEM	POST. REF.	DEBIT	DATE	ITEM	POST. REF.	CREDIT
19-- Nov.	1	Balance	J1	3 250 00				

ACCOUNT **Office Furniture** — — — — — — — — — — — — — — — — — ACCOUNT NO. **13**

DATE		ITEM	POST. REF.	DEBIT	DATE		ITEM	POST. REF.	CREDIT
19-- Nov.	1	Balance	J1	650 00	19-- Nov.	25		C2	35 00
	11		C2	45 00					

ACCOUNT **Office Equipment** — — — — — — — — — — — — — — — — — ACCOUNT NO. **14**

DATE		ITEM	POST. REF.	DEBIT	DATE	ITEM	POST. REF.	CREDIT
19-- Nov.	1	Balance	J1	420 00				
	30		C2	370 00				

ACCOUNT **Martin Supplies, Inc.** — — — — — — — — — — — — — — — ACCOUNT NO. **21**

DATE		ITEM	POST. REF.	DEBIT	DATE		ITEM	POST. REF.	CREDIT
19-- Nov.	7		C2	79 75	19-- Nov.	1	Balance	J1	79 75

ACCOUNT **Samson Company** — — — — — — — — — — — — — — — — — ACCOUNT NO. **22**

DATE		ITEM	POST. REF.	DEBIT	DATE		ITEM	POST. REF.	CREDIT
19-- Nov.	28		C2	100 00	19-- Nov.	1	Balance	J1	459 57

LEDGER

ACCOUNT *Wilson Company*   ACCOUNT NO. 23

DATE	ITEM	POST. REF.	DEBIT	DATE	ITEM	POST. REF.	CREDIT
19-- Nov. 25		C2	21545	19-- Nov. 1	Balance	J1	31545

ACCOUNT *Harry Gordon, Capital*   ACCOUNT NO. 31

DATE	ITEM	POST. REF.	DEBIT	DATE	ITEM	POST. REF.	CREDIT
				19-- Nov. 1	Balance	J1	425023

ACCOUNT *Fees Revenue*   ACCOUNT NO. 41

DATE	ITEM	POST. REF.	DEBIT	DATE	ITEM	POST. REF.	CREDIT
				19-- Nov. 30		C2	160050

ACCOUNT *Automobile Expense*   ACCOUNT NO. 51

DATE	ITEM	POST. REF.	DEBIT	DATE	ITEM	POST. REF.	CREDIT
19-- Nov. 11		C2	1439				
16		C2	1349				
24		C2	1350				
29		C2	1260				

ACCOUNT *Miscellaneous Expense*   ACCOUNT NO. 52

DATE	ITEM	POST. REF.	DEBIT	DATE	ITEM	POST. REF.	CREDIT
19-- Nov. 9		C2	2130				
16		C2	915				
22		C2	5180				
29		C2	6125				
30		C2	1238				

LEDGER

ACCOUNT Rent Expense   ACCOUNT NO. 53

DATE	ITEM	POST. REF.	DEBIT	DATE	ITEM	POST. REF.	CREDIT
19-- Nov. 1		C2	175 00				

ACCOUNT Supplies Expense   ACCOUNT NO. 54

DATE	ITEM	POST. REF.	DEBIT	DATE	ITEM	POST. REF.	CREDIT
19-- Nov. 4		C2	40 37				
14		C2	84 26				
21		C2	33 14				

ACCOUNT Telephone Expense   ACCOUNT NO. 55

DATE	ITEM	POST. REF.	DEBIT	DATE	ITEM	POST. REF.	CREDIT
19-- Nov. 30		C2	10 30				

[3]

ACCOUNT TITLE	ACCT. NO.	DEBIT	CREDIT

JOURNALIZING, POSTING, AND TAKING A TRIAL BALANCE

[2, 3]

GENERAL JOURNAL   PAGE_____

	DATE		ACCOUNT TITLE	POST. REF.	DEBIT	CREDIT	
1							1
2							2
3							3
4							4
5							5
6							6
7							7
8							8
9							9
10							10
11							11
12							12
13							13
14							14
15							15
16							16
17							17
18							18
19							19
20							20
21							21
22							22
23							23
24							24
25							25
26							26
27							27
28							28
29							29
30							30
31							31
32							32

CASH JOURNAL   PAGE

	1	2					3	4	5	
	CASH DEBIT	GENERAL DEBIT	DATE	ACCOUNT TITLE	NO.	POST. REF.	GENERAL CREDIT	ROOM SALES CREDIT	CASH CREDIT	
1										1
2										2
3										3
4										4
5										5
6										6
7										7
8										8
9										9
10										10
11										11
12										12
13										13
14										14
15										15
16										16
17										17
18										18
19										19
20										20
21										21
22										22
23										23
24										24
25										25
26										26
27										27
28										28
29										29
30										30
31										31
32										32
33										33

[7] *Proving equality of debits and credits:*

Cash Debit footing......................$_____

General Debit footing.................... _____

Total debits..............................$_____

General Credit footing...................$_____

Room Sales Credit footing............... _____

Cash Credit footing...................... _____

Total credits.............................$_____

[8] *Prove cash:*

Cash balance, February 1, 19—...........$_____

+ Cash received, February 1–28, 19—........ _____

Total of beginning balance+cash received .$_____

− Cash paid, February 1–28, 19—............ _____

Cash on hand, February 28, 19—..........$_____

ACCOUNT TITLE	ACCT. NO.	DEBIT	CREDIT

ACCOUNT TITLE	ACCT. No.	DEBIT	CREDIT

LEDGER

ACCOUNT _____ ACCOUNT NO. _____

DATE	ITEM	POST. REF.	DEBIT	DATE	ITEM	POST. REF.	CREDIT

ACCOUNT _____ ACCOUNT NO. _____

DATE	ITEM	POST. REF.	DEBIT	DATE	ITEM	POST. REF.	CREDIT

ACCOUNT _____ ACCOUNT NO. _____

DATE	ITEM	POST. REF.	DEBIT	DATE	ITEM	POST. REF.	CREDIT

ACCOUNT _____ ACCOUNT NO. _____

DATE	ITEM	POST. REF.	DEBIT	DATE	ITEM	POST. REF.	CREDIT

LEDGER

ACCOUNT _____   ACCOUNT NO. _____

DATE	ITEM	POST. REF.	DEBIT	DATE	ITEM	POST. REF.	CREDIT

ACCOUNT _____   ACCOUNT NO. _____

DATE	ITEM	POST. REF.	DEBIT	DATE	ITEM	POST. REF.	CREDIT

ACCOUNT _____   ACCOUNT NO. _____

DATE	ITEM	POST. REF.	DEBIT	DATE	ITEM	POST. REF.	CREDIT

ACCOUNT _____   ACCOUNT NO. _____

DATE	ITEM	POST. REF.	DEBIT	DATE	ITEM	POST. REF.	CREDIT

LEDGER

ACCOUNT _____ ACCOUNT NO. _____

DATE		ITEM	POST. REF.	DEBIT	DATE		ITEM	POST. REF.	CREDIT

ACCOUNT _____ ACCOUNT NO. _____

DATE		ITEM	POST. REF.	DEBIT	DATE		ITEM	POST. REF.	CREDIT

ACCOUNT _____ ACCOUNT NO. _____

DATE		ITEM	POST. REF.	DEBIT	DATE		ITEM	POST. REF.	CREDIT

ACCOUNT _____ ACCOUNT NO. _____

DATE		ITEM	POST. REF.	DEBIT	DATE		ITEM	POST. REF.	CREDIT

ACCOUNT _____ ACCOUNT NO. _____

DATE		ITEM	POST. REF.	DEBIT	DATE		ITEM	POST. REF.	CREDIT

LEDGER

ACCOUNT _____ ACCOUNT NO. _____

DATE	ITEM	POST. REF.	DEBIT	DATE	ITEM	POST. REF.	CREDIT

ACCOUNT _____ ACCOUNT NO. _____

DATE	ITEM	POST. REF.	DEBIT	DATE	ITEM	POST. REF.	CREDIT

ACCOUNT _____ ACCOUNT NO. _____

DATE	ITEM	POST. REF.	DEBIT	DATE	ITEM	POST. REF.	CREDIT

ACCOUNT _____ ACCOUNT NO. _____

DATE	ITEM	POST. REF.	DEBIT	DATE	ITEM	POST. REF.	CREDIT

Perfect Score..46	Name_____	STUDY GUIDE
Deduct.......—	Date_____ Class_____	
Your Score...—	Checked by_____	

Unit A—Business Vocabulary

DIRECTIONS: Complete each item in Column II by selecting one of the terms given in Column I. Then print the identifying letter of that term in the Answers column.

A — analysis paper

B — balance sheet

C — fiscal period

D — fiscal year

E — ledger

F — net income

G — net loss

H — proving cash

I — trial balance

J — work sheet

Item		Answers	For Scoring
0.	The length of time for which an analysis of business operations is made is called a..........	C	0. ✓
1.	An accounting period of twelve consecutive months is called a.............		1.
2.	The proof of the equality of the debits and credits in the ledger is called a..........		2.
3.	Analysis paper on which the financial condition of a business is summarized is called a.........		3.
4.	When the total expenses are larger than the total revenue, the difference is called.........		4.
5.	Accounting paper with a number of amount columns that can be used to sort and analyze information is called......		5.
6.	When the total revenue is larger than the total expenses, the amount of the difference is called..........		6.

Unit B—Entering Account Balances in the Trial Balance Columns

DIRECTIONS: After each account title, place a check mark in the proper Trial Balance Debit or Credit column to indicate where its account balance should appear.

Account	Trial Balance Debit	Trial Balance Credit	For Scoring
0. Cash...............	✓		0. ✓
7. Operating Supplies....			7.
8. Car Wash Equipment..			8.
9. Office Equipment.....			9.
10. Auto Wash Equipment Company (creditor) .			10.

Account	Trial Balance Debit	Trial Balance Credit	For Scoring
11. Marco Plumbing Company (creditor).....			11.
12. Harry Shaw, Capital...			12.
13. Sales................			13.
14. Advertising Expense...			14.
15. Fuel Expense.........			15.
16. Miscellaneous Expense.			16.
17. Rent Expense.........			17.
18. Utilities Expense......			18.

Unit C—Sorting Account Balances on the Work Sheet

DIRECTIONS: After each account title, place a check mark in the column in which the account balance would be extended on the work sheet.

Account	Income Statement Debit	Income Statement Credit	Balance Sheet Debit	Balance Sheet Credit	For Scoring
0. Cash...............................			✓		0. ✓
19. Operating Supplies.....................					19.
20. Car Wash Equipment...................					20.
21. Office Equipment.....................					21.
22. Auto Wash Equipment Company (creditor)........					22.
23. Marco Plumbing Company (creditor).............					23.
24. Harry Shaw, Capital....................					24.
25. Sales.............................					25.
26. Advertising Expense...................					26.
27. Fuel Expense.......................					27.
28. Miscellaneous Expense.................					28.
29. Rent Expense.......................					29.
30. Utilities Expense.....................					30.

DIRECTIONS: For each of the following items, select the answer that best completes the sentence. Then print in the Answers column at the right the capital letter identifying your choice.

	Answers	For Scoring
0. The work sheet summarizes the financial condition of a business for a **(A)** future fiscal period **(B)** past fiscal period **(C)** specific date..................	B	0. ✓
31. The information written on the third line of the work sheet's heading is the **(A)** name of the form **(B)** length and the closing date of the fiscal period for which the analysis is made **(C)** name of the business........................		31.
32. Two columns of the work sheet that are used to enter asset account balances are **(A)** Trial Balance Credit and Balance Sheet Debit **(B)** Trial Balance Debit and Balance Sheet Credit **(C)** Trial Balance Debit and Balance Sheet Debit....................		32.
33. The two columns of the work sheet in which liability account balances are written are **(A)** Trial Balance Debit and Balance Sheet Debit **(B)** Trial Balance Credit and Balance Sheet Credit **(C)** Trial Balance Credit and Income Statement Credit........		33.
34. Two columns of the work sheet that are used to enter the capital account balance are **(A)** Trial Balance Debit and Balance Sheet Credit **(B)** Trial Balance Credit and Income Statement Credit **(C)** Trial Balance Credit and Balance Sheet Credit........		34.
35. The two columns of the work sheet in which the amount of each expense is listed are **(A)** Trial Balance Debit and Balance Sheet Debit **(B)** Trial Balance Debit and Income Statement Debit **(C)** Trial Balance Debit and Income Statement Credit......		35.
36. Two columns of the work sheet that are used to list the amount of each revenue are **(A)** Trial Balance Credit and Balance Sheet Debit **(B)** Trial Balance Credit and Balance Sheet Credit **(C)** Trial Balance Credit and Income Statement Credit........		36.
37. In the Trial Balance section of the work sheet, the balance of each liability account is shown in **(A)** the Debit column **(B)** the Credit column **(C)** neither of the two Trial Balance columns...........................		37.
38. In the Income Statement section of the work sheet, the balance of each asset account is shown in **(A)** the Debit column **(B)** the Credit column **(C)** neither of the two Income Statement columns................		38.
39. In the Balance Sheet section of the work sheet, the balance of each revenue account is shown in **(A)** the Debit column **(B)** the Credit column **(C)** neither of the two Balance Sheet columns...........................		39.
40. The amount of net income obtained in the Income Statement section of the work sheet is extended into the Balance Sheet Credit column because it increases **(A)** assets **(B)** capital **(C)** liabilities..........................		40.
41. When the total of the Debit column of the Income Statement section of the work sheet is larger than the total of the Credit column, the difference is called a **(A)** net income **(B)** net loss **(C)** net result....................		41.
42. Two columns of the work sheet that are used to enter the amount of a net income are **(A)** Income Statement Credit and Balance Sheet Debit **(B)** Income Statement Debit and Balance Sheet Debit **(C)** Income Statement Debit and Balance Sheet Credit.....		42.
43. When the total of the Credit column of the Income Statement section of the work sheet is larger than the total of the Debit column, the difference is called a **(A)** net worth **(B)** net loss **(C)** net income....................		43.
44. The two columns of the work sheet in which the amount of a net loss is written are **(A)** Income Statement Credit and Balance Sheet Debit **(B)** Income Statement Credit and Balance Sheet Credit **(C)** Income Statement Debit and Balance Sheet Debit.....		44.
45. On the work sheet, a comparison of the difference between the totals of the Income Statement columns and the difference between the totals of the Balance Sheet columns should show the **(A)** difference between the Income Statement columns to be larger **(B)** difference between the Balance Sheet columns to be larger **(C)** differences to be the same.......		45.
46. The final step in preparing a six-column work sheet is to **(A)** rule a single line across all the amount columns and add these columns **(B)** rule double lines below the final totals of the Income Statement columns and the Balance Sheet columns **(C)** write *Net Income* in the Account Title column on the same line as the net income amount....................		46.

Sorting account balances on the work sheet

	3	4	5	6
Account Title	Income Statement		Balance Sheet	
	Debit	Credit	Debit	Credit
1. Advertising Expense...............................	√			
2.				
3.				
4.				
5.				
6.				
7.				
8.				
9.				
10.				
11.				
12.				
13.				
14.				
15.				

Work sheet for a real estate agency

Problem 9-1 is continued in the next chapter. Your teacher will return this work sheet to you before it is needed in Problem 10-1.

Work sheet for a travel agency

ACCOUNT TITLE	ACCT. NO.	TRIAL BALANCE		INCOME STATEMENT		BALANCE SHEET	
		1 DEBIT	2 CREDIT	3 DEBIT	4 CREDIT	5 DEBIT	6 CREDIT
1							
2							
3							
4							
5							
6							
7							
8							
9							
10							
11							
12							
13							
14							
15							
16							
17							
18							
19							
20							
21							
22							
23							
24							
25							

Work sheet for a theater

ACCOUNT TITLE	ACCT. NO.	TRIAL BALANCE		INCOME STATEMENT		BALANCE SHEET	
		1 DEBIT	2 CREDIT	3 DEBIT	4 CREDIT	5 DEBIT	6 CREDIT
1							
2							
3							
4							
5							
6							
7							
8							
9							
10							
11							
12							
13							
14							
15							
16							
17							
18							
19							
20							
21							
22							
23							
24							
25							

Perfect Score..46

Deduct.......—

Your Score...—

Name_____

Date_____ Class_____

Checked by_____

Unit A—Locating Data on an Income Statement

DIRECTIONS: Locate where each of the following items is written on the income statement illustrated below by printing the proper identifying letter in the Answers column.

A
B
C
D
E   J
F
G   K
H   L
I   M

	Answers	For Scoring
0. Period of time covered.....	C	0. ✓
1. Section heading *Revenue*....		1.
2. Section heading *Expenses*...		2.
3. Titles of the individual expense accounts........		3.
4. Amount of the net loss.....		4.
5. Words *Total Expenses*......		5.
6. Words *Net Income*........		6.
7. Amount of each expense item.................		7.
8. Name of the financial statement.............		8.
9. Words *Income Statement*.....		9.
10. Name of the business......		10.
11. Amount of the net income..		11.
12. Words *Net Loss*...........		12.
13. Total amount of expenses...		13.
14. Title of the revenue account		14.
15. Amount of the revenue item		15.

Unit B—Locating Data on a Balance Sheet

DIRECTIONS: Locate where each of the following items is written on the balance sheet illustrated below by printing the proper identifying letter in the Answers column.

A
B
C
D   I
E   G J   O
      K   P
      L
     M   Q
F   H N   R

	Answers	For Scoring
0. Name of the business......	A	0. ✓
16. Section heading *Capital*....		16.
17. Title of capital account....		17.
18. Section heading *Liabilities*..		18.
19. Amount of each asset item..		19.
20. Words *Total Assets*........		20.
21. Words *Total Liab. and Capital*................		21.
22. Title of each liability......		22.
23. Total amount of assets.....		23.
24. Specific date of financial statement.............		24.
25. Total amount of liabilities..		25.
26. Name of the financial statement.............		26.
27. Words *Total Liabilities*.....		27.
28. Total amount of liabilities and capital...........		28.
29. Amount of each liability item.................		29.
30. Section heading *Assets*.....		30.
31. Amount of capital........		31.
32. Title of each asset account..		32.

Chapter 10 ■ 83

DIRECTIONS: For each of the following items, select the answer that best completes the sentence. Then print in the Answers column at the right the capital letter identifying your choice.

	Answers	For Scoring

0. The income statement is a report that shows the
(A) financial progress of a business for a fiscal period   (B) financial condition of a business on a particular date   (C) net worth of a business for a past fiscal period . . . . . .   *A*   0. √

33. The income statement shows the revenue, the expenses, and the net income (or the net loss) of a business
(A) from the time the business was started   (B) for a certain fiscal period
(C) for a specific date . . . .   33.

34. The most convenient source for obtaining all of the amounts needed on the income statement would be the
(A) Debit and Credit columns of the accounts in the general ledger
(B) Income Statement columns of the work sheet
(C) Debit and Credit columns of the Trial Balance section of the work sheet . . . .   34.

35. The most convenient source for obtaining the names of all accounts to be listed on the income statement normally would be the
(A) Account Title column of the cash journal   (B) each page of the general ledger
(C) Account Title column of the work sheet . . . .   35.

36. The amounts for preparing the revenue section of the income statement are obtained directly from the
(A) Trial Balance columns of the work sheet
(B) Income Statement Debit column of the work sheet
(C) Income Statement Credit column of the work sheet . . . .   36.

37. In preparing an income statement, the last section to be listed is the
(A) expenses section   (B) revenue section   (C) assets section . . . .   37.

38. Net income is the difference that results on the income statement when the
(A) revenue items are subtracted from the expense items
(B) total of the revenue section is larger than the total of the expenses section
(C) total of the expenses section is larger than the total of the revenue section . . . .   38.

39. The amounts for preparing the expenses section of the income statement are obtained directly from the
(A) Trial Balance columns of the work sheet
(B) Income Statement Debit column of the work sheet
(C) Income Statement Credit column of the work sheet . . . .   39.

40. All calculations on the income statement are assumed to be correct when the net income amount on the income statement agrees with the
(A) total of the Income Statement Credit column of the work sheet
(B) net income amount in the Income Statement Debit column of the work sheet
(C) total of the Trial Balance Credit column of the work sheet . . . .   40.

41. Net loss is the difference that results on the income statement when the
(A) total of the revenue section is larger than the total of the expenses section
(B) revenue items exceed the expense items
(C) total of the expenses section is larger than the total of the revenue section . . . .   41.

42. The balance sheet is a report that shows the
(A) financial condition of a business on a particular date   (B) financial progress of a business for a fiscal period   (C) net income of a business for a past fiscal period . . . .   42.

43. The balance sheet lists all the assets, liabilities, and capital of a business
(A) for a particular period of time that has elapsed   (B) on a specific date
(C) for a particular period of time in the future . . . .   43.

44. The amounts for the capital section of the balance sheet are obtained from the
(A) Trial Balance Credit column of the work sheet   (B) Income Statement Credit column of the work sheet   (C) Balance Sheet columns of the work sheet . . . .   44.

45. The amounts for the liabilities section of the balance sheet are obtained from the
(A) Balance Sheet Credit column of the work sheet   (B) Income Statement Credit column of the work sheet   (C) Trial Balance Credit column of the work sheet . . . .   45.

46. The amounts for the assets section of the balance sheet are obtained from the
(A) Trial Balance Debit column of the work sheet   (B) Income Statement Debit column of the work sheet   (C) Balance Sheet Debit column of the work sheet . . . .   46.

Name_____Date_____Class_____

Work sheet for a bowling center   [1]

	ACCT. NO.	TRIAL BALANCE		INCOME STATEMENT		BALANCE SHEET	
ACCOUNT TITLE		1 DEBIT	2 CREDIT	3 DEBIT	4 CREDIT	5 DEBIT	6 CREDIT
1							
2							
3							
4							
5							
6							
7							
8							
9							
10							
11							
12							
13							
14							
15							
16							
17							
18							
19							
20							
21							
22							
23							
24							
25							

ACCOUNT TITLE	ACCT. NO.	TRIAL BALANCE		INCOME STATEMENT		BALANCE SHEET	
		DEBIT 1	CREDIT 2	DEBIT 3	CREDIT 4	DEBIT 5	CREDIT 6
1							
2							
3							
4							
5							
6							
7							
8							
9							
10							
11							
12							
13							
14							
15							
16							
17							
18							
19							
20							
21							
22							
23							
24							
25							

Financial reports for a bowling center

[1]

Financial reports for an automobile driving school

[2]

[1]

[2]

Perfect Score..32

Deduct........—

Your Score...—

Name _____

Date _____ Class _____

Checked by _____

Unit A — Business Vocabulary

DIRECTIONS: Complete each item in Column II by selecting one of the terms given in Column I. Then print the identifying letter of that term in the Answers column.

Column I	Column II	Answers	For Scoring
A — accounting cycle	0. Analysis paper on which the financial condition of a business is conveniently summarized is called a.................	*N*	0. ✓
B — balance sheet	1. An entry that contains two or more debits or two or more credits is called a................................		1.
C — balancing an account	2. After the closing entries are posted, an account with a balance remaining is called an...................		2.
D — "clearing" account	3. The process of transferring the balances of the revenue and expense accounts through a summary account to the proprietor's capital account is called.................		3.
E — closed account			
F — closing entry	4. The complete series of activities involved in double-entry accounting during a fiscal period is called the...........		4.
G — closing the ledger			
H — combined entry	5. An entry that transfers the balance from one account to another is called a................................		5.
I — Income Summary	6. The trial balance taken after the closing entries have been posted is called a.............................		6.
J — open account			
K — opening entry	7. An account that has had a balance transferred to another account is called a.............................		7.
L — post-closing trial balance	8. The process of determining the balance of an account, and bringing the balance into the new section of the account is called..................		8.
M — ruling an account			
N — work sheet	9. The account to which the balance of each revenue and each expense account is transferred at the end of the fiscal period is called..................................		9.

Unit B — Closing the Ledger

DIRECTIONS: For each of the following closing entries, indicate the accounts to be debited and credited by writing the account numbers in the Debit and Credit columns. Select the account numbers from the list given below at the left. Only the accounts needed for the closing entries are given in this list.

ACCOUNT TITLE	ACCT. NO.
FOR SAMPLE 0-0:	
INCOME SUMMARY...........	32
SALES.........................	41
FOR QUESTIONS 10-17:	
SALLY GRANT, CAPITAL.........	31
INCOME SUMMARY.............	32
COMMISSIONS REVENUE........	41
ADVERTISING EXPENSE.........	51
LAUNDRY EXPENSE............	52
MISCELLANEOUS EXPENSE......	53
RENT EXPENSE................	54
UTILITIES EXPENSE............	55

Entry to close the:	Answers Debit	Answers Credit	For Scoring Debit	For Scoring Credit
0-0. Sales account..........	41	32	0. ✓	0. ✓
10-11. Commissions revenue account.............			10.	11.
12-13. All the expense accounts			12.	13.
14-15. Income summary account (net loss)...........			14.	15.
16-17. Income summary account (net income)........			16.	17.

DIRECTIONS: For each of the following items, select the answer that best completes the sentence. Then print in the Answers column at the right the capital letter identifying your choice.

	Answers	For Scoring

0. The account to which the balance of each revenue and each expense account is transferred at the end of the fiscal period is titled
(A) Harry Shaw, Capital (B) Income Summary (C) Sales. | *B* | 0. ✓

18. The division of the ledger in which the income summary account is placed is the
(A) liabilities division (B) capital division (C) assets division. . . . . | | 18.

19. After the closing entries have been posted, the sales account shows
(A) no balance (B) a credit balance (C) a debit balance. . . . . | | 19.

20. After the closing entries have been posted, the utilities expense account shows
(A) a credit balance (B) no balance (C) a debit balance. | | 20.

21. After the closing entries have been posted, the income summary account shows
(A) a credit balance (B) a debit balance (C) no balance. . . . . | | 21.

22. After the closing entries have been posted, the amount of the net income appears in the
(A) income summary account on the credit side (B) owner's capital account on the debit side (C) owner's capital account on the credit side. . . . . | | 22.

23. After the closing entries have been posted, the amount of a net loss would appear in the
(A) income summary account on the debit side (B) owner's capital account on the debit side (C) owner's capital account on the credit side. . . . . | | 23.

24. The information necessary for closing all revenue accounts is found in the
(A) Income Statement Credit column of the work sheet (B) Trial Balance Credit column of the work sheet (C) Balance Sheet Debit column of the work sheet. . . . . | | 24.

25. The information necessary for closing the expense accounts is found in the
(A) Balance Sheet Credit column of the work sheet (B) Income Statement Debit column of the work sheet (C) Trial Balance Debit column of the work sheet. . . . . | | 25.

26. The balance of the income summary account is the net income for the fiscal period when
(A) the credit side has the larger footing (B) both sides have equal footings
(C) the credit side has the smaller footing. . . . . | | 26.

27. The balance of the income summary account is the net loss for the fiscal period when
(A) both sides have equal footings (B) the debit side has the larger footing
(C) the debit side has the smaller footing. . . . . | | 27.

28. A debit balance in the income summary account before it is closed into the owner's capital account indicates that there has been
(A) a net decrease in capital (B) neither an increase nor a decrease in capital (C) a net increase in income. . . . . | | 28.

29. A credit balance in the income summary account before it is closed into the owner's capital account indicates
(A) neither an increase nor a decrease in income (B) a net increase in capital
(C) a net decrease in income. . . . . | | 29.

30. After the closing entries have been posted, the balance of the owner's capital account should agree with the amount of the
(A) capital on the balance sheet (B) revenue for the fiscal period
(C) net income for the fiscal period. . . . . | | 30.

31. The only accounts that are listed on the post-closing trial balance are those that
(A) are open at the end of the fiscal period (B) have no balances
(C) are closed at the end of the fiscal period. . . . . | | 31.

32. After the closing entries have been posted and the accounts have been balanced and ruled, a post-closing trial balance is taken to
(A) see if the owner's capital account now agrees with the amount of revenue shown on the income statement (B) see if the balance of the owner's capital account agrees with the balance of the income summary account
(C) test the equality of debits and credits in the ledger. . . . . | | 32.

Identifying accounts as open or closed after closing entries are posted

Account Title	Answers		Account Title	Answers
1. *Delivery Revenue*	*C*	9.		
2.		10.		
3.		11.		
4.		12.		
5.		13.		
6.		14.		
7.		15.		
8.		16.		

Analyzing amounts that affect total capital during a fiscal period

Business	Balance in Capital Account at Start of Period	Additional Investment by Owner During Period	Net Income (+) or Net Loss (−) During Period	Balance in Capital Account after Ledger is Closed
1.	$13,500.00	$1,500.00	+ $4,640.00	$19,640.00
2.	28,000.00	None	− 1,860.00	26,140.00
3.	42,600.00	3,000.00	+ 6,450.00	
4.	18,300.00	2,500.00	+ 3,380.00	
5.	32,400.00	None	− 1,480.00	
6.	23,800.00	1,800.00	− 1,250.00	
7.	52,000.00	4,500.00		53,460.00
8.	38,850.00	None		43,200.00
9.	74,000.00	5,500.00		83,330.00
10.	36,880.00		+ 2,640.00	42,520.00
11.	92,500.00		− 1,380.00	92,620.00
12.		None	+ 2,370.00	26,830.00

Recording closing entries in a general journal

PROBLEM 11-1, p. 160

GENERAL JOURNAL

PAGE 20

	DATE		ACCOUNT TITLE	POST. REF.	DEBIT	CREDIT	
1							1
2							2
3							3
4							4
5							5
6							6
7							7
8							8
9							9
10							10
11							11
12							12
13							13
14							14
15							15

Recording closing entries in a general journal

PROBLEM 11-2, p. 160

GENERAL JOURNAL

PAGE 46

	DATE		ACCOUNT TITLE	POST. REF.	DEBIT	CREDIT	
1							1
2							2
3							3
4							4
5							5
6							6
7							7
8							8
9							9
10							10
11							11
12							12
13							13
14							14
15							15

Name_____Date_____Class_____

Closing the ledger

ACCOUNT **Cash** ACCOUNT NO. *11*

DATE	ITEM	POST. REF.	DEBIT	DATE	ITEM	POST. REF.	CREDIT
Sept. 1	Balance	J1	123886	Sept. 30		C2	268054
30		C2	326538				

ACCOUNT **Delivery Equipment** ACCOUNT NO. *12*

DATE	ITEM	POST. REF.	DEBIT	DATE	ITEM	POST. REF.	CREDIT
Sept. 1	Balance	J1	545000	Sept. 4		C1	31800
18		C1	74000				

ACCOUNT **Office Equipment** ACCOUNT NO. *13*

DATE	ITEM	POST. REF.	DEBIT	DATE	ITEM	POST. REF.	CREDIT
Sept. 1	Balance	J1	38875				

ACCOUNT **Cain Brothers, Inc.** ACCOUNT NO. *21*

DATE	ITEM	POST. REF.	DEBIT	DATE	ITEM	POST. REF.	CREDIT
Sept. 12		C1	10000	Sept. 1	Balance	J1	40000

ACCOUNT **Jackson Supply Company** ACCOUNT NO. *22*

DATE	ITEM	POST. REF.	DEBIT	DATE	ITEM	POST. REF.	CREDIT
Sept. 22		C1	63550	Sept. 1	Balance	J1	116281

LEDGER

ACCOUNT *David Kiley, Capital*   ACCOUNT NO. 31

DATE	ITEM	POST. REF.	DEBIT	DATE	ITEM	POST. REF.	CREDIT
				Sept. 1	Balance	J1	5589 43

ACCOUNT *Income Summary*   ACCOUNT NO. 32

DATE	ITEM	POST. REF.	DEBIT	DATE	ITEM	POST. REF.	CREDIT

ACCOUNT *Fees Revenue*   ACCOUNT NO. 41

DATE	ITEM	POST. REF.	DEBIT	DATE	ITEM	POST. REF.	CREDIT
				Sept. 30		C2	3042 50

ACCOUNT *Delivery Expense*   ACCOUNT NO. 51

DATE	ITEM	POST. REF.	DEBIT	DATE	ITEM	POST. REF.	CREDIT
Sept. 30		C2	940 00				

ACCOUNT *Miscellaneous Expense*   ACCOUNT NO. 52

DATE	ITEM	POST. REF.	DEBIT	DATE	ITEM	POST. REF.	CREDIT
Sept. 15		C1	46 25				
30		C2	38 54				

ACCOUNT *Rent Expense*   ACCOUNT NO. 53

DATE	ITEM	POST. REF.	DEBIT	DATE	ITEM	POST. REF.	CREDIT
Sept. 30		C2	350 00				

[3]

ACCOUNT TITLE	ACCT. NO.	TRIAL BALANCE		INCOME STATEMENT		BALANCE SHEET	
		DEBIT	CREDIT	DEBIT	CREDIT	DEBIT	CREDIT
		1	2	3	4	5	6

Extra form

ACCOUNT TITLE	ACCT. NO.	TRIAL BALANCE		INCOME STATEMENT		BALANCE SHEET	
		1 DEBIT	2 CREDIT	3 DEBIT	4 CREDIT	5 DEBIT	6 CREDIT
1							
2							
3							
4							
5							
6							
7							
8							
9							
10							
11							
12							
13							
14							
15							
16							
17							
18							
19							
20							
21							
22							
23							
24							
25							

[5]

[6]

GENERAL JOURNAL

PAGE

DATE	ACCOUNT TITLE	POST. REF.	DEBIT	CREDIT	
1					1
2					2
3					3
4					4
5					5
6					6
7					7
8					8
9					9
10					10
11					11
12					12
13					13
14					14

[10]

ACCOUNT TITLE	ACCT. NO.	DEBIT	CREDIT

THE COMPLETE ACCOUNTING CYCLE

CASH JOURNAL   PAGE_____

	CASH DEBIT	GENERAL DEBIT	DATE	ACCOUNT TITLE	NO.	POST. REF.	GENERAL CREDIT	DRY CLEANING SALES CREDIT	LAUNDRY SALES CREDIT	CASH CREDIT	
	1	2					3	4	5	6	
1											1
2											2
3											3
4											4
5											5
6											6
7											7
8											8
9											9
10											10
11											11
12											12
13											13
14											14
15											15
16											16
17											17
18											18
19											19
20											20
21											21
22											22
23											23
24											24
25											25
26											26
27											27
28											28
29											29
30											30
31											31
32											32
33											33
34											34
35											35
36											36
37											37
38											38

[6] *Proving equality of debits and credits:*

Cash Debit footing.......................$_____

General Debit footing................... _____

Total debits............................$_____

General Credit footing.................$_____

Dry Cleaning Sales Credit footing........ _____

Laundry Sales Credit footing............ _____

Cash Credit footing..................... _____

Total credits...........................$_____

[7] *Prove cash:*

Cash balance, March 1, 19—..............$_____

+ Cash received, March 1–31, 19—.......... _____

Total of beginning balance+cash received .$_____

− Cash paid, March 1–31, 19—.............. _____

Cash on hand, March 31, 19—.............$_____

[16]

GENERAL JOURNAL

PAGE

	DATE		ACCOUNT TITLE	POST. REF.	DEBIT	CREDIT	
1							1
2							2
3							3
4							4
5							5
6							6
7							7
8							8
9							9
10							10
11							11
12							12
13							13
14							14
15							15
16							16

[12, 13]

ACCOUNT TITLE	ACCT. NO.	TRIAL BALANCE		INCOME STATEMENT		BALANCE SHEET	
		DEBIT	CREDIT	DEBIT	CREDIT	DEBIT	CREDIT
		1	2	3	4	5	6

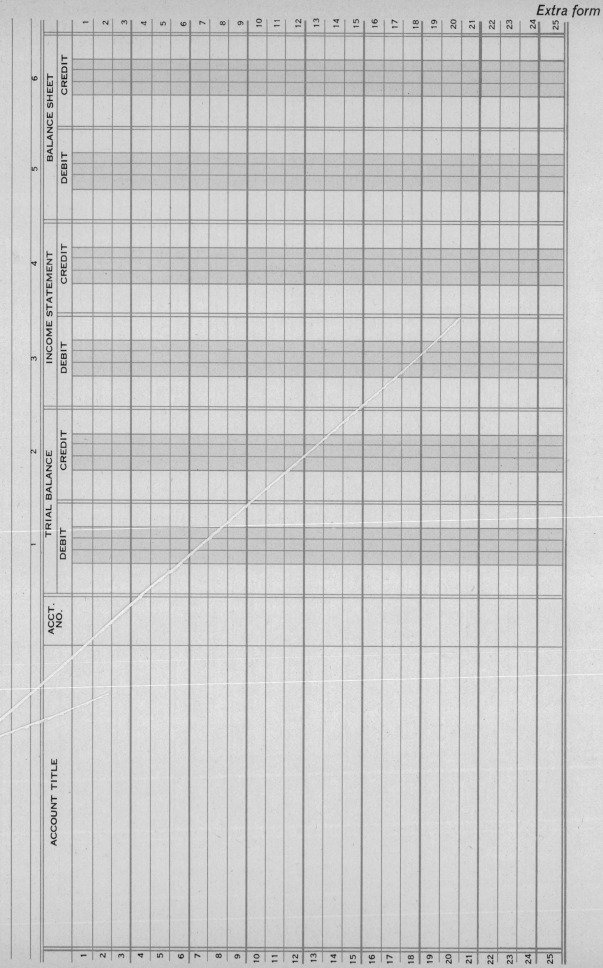

LEDGER

ACCOUNT _____ ACCOUNT NO. _____

DATE	ITEM	POST. REF.	DEBIT	DATE	ITEM	POST. REF.	CREDIT

ACCOUNT _____ ACCOUNT NO. _____

DATE	ITEM	POST. REF.	DEBIT	DATE	ITEM	POST. REF.	CREDIT

ACCOUNT _____ ACCOUNT NO. _____

DATE	ITEM	POST. REF.	DEBIT	DATE	ITEM	POST. REF.	CREDIT

ACCOUNT _____ ACCOUNT NO. _____

DATE	ITEM	POST. REF.	DEBIT	DATE	ITEM	POST. REF.	CREDIT

LEDGER

ACCOUNT _____ ACCOUNT NO. _____

DATE	ITEM	POST. REF.	DEBIT	DATE	ITEM	POST. REF.	CREDIT

ACCOUNT _____ ACCOUNT NO. _____

DATE	ITEM	POST. REF.	DEBIT	DATE	ITEM	POST. REF.	CREDIT

ACCOUNT _____ ACCOUNT NO. _____

DATE	ITEM	POST. REF.	DEBIT	DATE	ITEM	POST. REF.	CREDIT

ACCOUNT _____ ACCOUNT NO. _____

DATE	ITEM	POST. REF.	DEBIT	DATE	ITEM	POST. REF.	CREDIT

LEDGER

ACCOUNT _____ ACCOUNT NO. _____

DATE	ITEM	POST. REF.	DEBIT	DATE	ITEM	POST. REF.	CREDIT

ACCOUNT _____ ACCOUNT NO. _____

DATE	ITEM	POST. REF.	DEBIT	DATE	ITEM	POST. REF.	CREDIT

ACCOUNT _____ ACCOUNT NO. _____

DATE	ITEM	POST. REF.	DEBIT	DATE	ITEM	POST. REF.	CREDIT

ACCOUNT _____ ACCOUNT NO. _____

DATE	ITEM	POST. REF.	DEBIT	DATE	ITEM	POST. REF.	CREDIT

ACCOUNT _____ ACCOUNT NO. _____

DATE	ITEM	POST. REF.	DEBIT	DATE	ITEM	POST. REF.	CREDIT

LEDGER

ACCOUNT _____ ACCOUNT NO. _____

DATE	ITEM	POST. REF.	DEBIT	DATE	ITEM	POST. REF.	CREDIT

ACCOUNT _____ ACCOUNT NO. _____

DATE	ITEM	POST. REF.	DEBIT	DATE	ITEM	POST. REF.	CREDIT

ACCOUNT _____ ACCOUNT NO. _____

DATE	ITEM	POST. REF.	DEBIT	DATE	ITEM	POST. REF.	CREDIT

ACCOUNT _____ ACCOUNT NO. _____

DATE	ITEM	POST. REF.	DEBIT	DATE	ITEM	POST. REF.	CREDIT

ACCOUNT TITLE	ACCT. NO.	DEBIT	CREDIT

[20]

Perfect Score..63

Deduct.......—

Your Score...—

Name_____

Date_____ Class_____

Checked by_____

STUDY GUIDE

Unit A—Business Vocabulary

DIRECTIONS: Complete each item in Column II by selecting the one term given in Column I that best completes the statement. Then print the identifying letter of that term in the Answers column.

Column I	Column II	Answers	For Scoring
A — cash sale	0. A person or firm to whom a business sells merchandise is called a..	*H*	0. √
B — charge customer	1. The account that shows the cost of merchandise purchased for resale to customers is called........................		1.
C — combination journal	2. A transaction in which merchandise is purchased with an agreement to pay at a later date is called a..............		2.
D — correcting entry	3. A business that buys and resells goods is called a.........		3.
E — cost of merchandise	4. The business from which merchandise is purchased on account is known as a...................................		4.
F — credit card	5. The value of goods a business purchases to resell to customers is called the...................................		5.
G — creditor	6. A person or business to whom a sale on account is made is called a..		6.
H — customer	7. A form describing the goods shipped, the method of shipment, the quantity and the price of the goods is called an..		7.
I — drawing account	8. A copy of an invoice that the seller uses as the source document for recording a sale of merchandise is called a......		8.
J — invoice	9. An embossed plastic plate identifying a customer with a charge account is called a...........................		9.
K — memorandum	10. A sales transaction with an agreement that merchandise will be paid for at a later date is called.................		10.
L — merchandise	11. The separate capital account in which all withdrawals are recorded is called a.................................		11.
M — merchandising business	12. The agreement between the buyer and the seller as to payment for merchandise is called the...................		12.
N — purchase invoice	13. A copy of an invoice that the buyer uses as the source document for recording the purchase of merchandise is called a..		13.
O — purchase of merchandise on account	14. A form prepared by a buyer describing what he desires to buy is called a.....................................		14.
P — purchase order	15. Assets taken out of a business for the personal use of the owner are called....................................		15.
Q — Purchases	16. A multicolumn journal that combines all journals into one book of original entry is called a.......................		16.
R — receipt	17. A form on which a brief interoffice message is written is called a...		17.
S — sale of merchandise on account	18. The goods that a merchandising business purchases for resale to customers are called.........................		18.
T — Sales	19. A journal entry made to correct an error in the ledger is called a...		19.
U — sales invoice			
V — terms of sale			
W — withdrawals			

Chapter 12 ▪ **113**

PAGE		COMBINATION JOURNAL				FOR MONTH OF		19	PAGE

CASH		DATE	ACCOUNT TITLE	Doc. No.	Post. Ref.	GENERAL		ACCOUNTS RECEIVABLE		SALES CREDIT	ACCOUNTS PAYABLE		PURCHASES DEBIT
DEBIT	CREDIT					DEBIT	CREDIT	DEBIT	CREDIT		DEBIT	CREDIT	
A	B	C	D	E	F	G	H	I	J	K	L	M	N

DIRECTIONS: Each column of the left and right pages of the combination journal illustrated above is identified with a capital letter. Complete each of the following statements by printing the capital letter that indicates the column of the combination journal in which the item should be recorded. The first five answers are supplied as examples.

A purchase of merchandise on account transaction is recorded by writing the

	Answers	For Scoring
0. date in	C	0. ✓
0. amount of the debit in	N	0. ✓
0. amount of the credit in	M	0. ✓
0. name of the creditor in	D	0. ✓
0. number of the purchase invoice in	E	0. ✓

A cash purchase of merchandise transaction is recorded by writing

	Answers	For Scoring
20. the date in		20.
21. the amount of the debit in		21.
22. the amount of the credit in		22.
23. a check mark in		23.
24. a check mark also in (to show that no individual amounts on this line need to be posted)		24.
25. the number of the check in		25.

A cash payment on account transaction is recorded by writing the

	Answers	For Scoring
26. date in		26.
27. amount of the debit in		27.
28. amount of the credit in		28.
29. name of the creditor in		29.
30. number of the check in		30.

A cash sales transaction is recorded by writing

	Answers	For Scoring
31. the date in		31.
32. the amount of the debit in		32.
33. the amount of the credit in		33.
34. a check mark in		34.
35. a check mark also in (to show that no individual amounts on this line need to be posted)		35.
36. the cash register tape number in		36.

A sale on account transaction is recorded by writing the

	Answers	For Scoring
37. date in		37.
38. amount of the debit in		38.
39. amount of the credit in		39.
40. name of the customer in		40.
41. number of the sales invoice in		41.

A cash received on account transaction is recorded by writing the

	Answers	For Scoring
42. date in		42.
43. amount of the debit in		43.
44. amount of the credit in		44.
45. name of the customer in		45.
46. number of the receipt in		46.

A cash payment of expense transaction is recorded by writing the

	Answers	For Scoring
47. date in		47.
48. amount of the debit in		48.
49. title of the account debited in		49.
50. amount of the credit in		50.
51. number of the check in		51.

A buying of supplies on account transaction is recorded by writing

	Answers	For Scoring
52. the date in		52.
53. the amount of the debit in		53.
54. the title of the account debited in		54.
55. the amount of the credit in		55.
56. the name of the creditor in		56.
57. a brace ({) in		57.
58. the number of the memorandum in		58.

A cash withdrawal by the owner transaction is recorded by writing the

	Answers	For Scoring
59. date in		59.
60. amount of the debit in		60.
61. title of the account debited in		61.
62. amount of the credit in		62.
63. number of the check in		63.

Analyzing transactions into their debit and credit parts

1.

Cash	
1,500.00	

Kent Houk, Capital	
	1,500.00

2.

3.

4.

5.

6.

7.

8.

9.

10.

11.

12.

13.

PAGE

COMBINATION JOURNAL

	1	2						3	4	
1										1
2										2
3										3
4										4
5										5
6										6
7										7
8										8
9										9
10										10
11										11
12										12
13										13
14										14
15										15
16										16
17										17
18										18
19										19
20										20
21										21
22										22
23										23
24										24
25										25
26										26
27										27
28										28
29										29
30										30
31										31
32										32
33										33

FOR MONTH OF _____ 19___ PAGE

	5	6	7	8	9	10

PAGE

COMBINATION JOURNAL

	CASH		DATE	ACCOUNT TITLE	Doc. No.	Post. Ref.	GENERAL	
	DEBIT	CREDIT					DEBIT	CREDIT
1								
2								
3								
4								
5								
6								
7								
8								
9								
10								
11								
12								
13								
14								
15								
16								
17								
18								
19								
20								
21								
22								
23								
24								
25								
26								
27								
28								
29								
30								
31								
32								
33								

Begin this problem on pages 120 and 121. Use this page with page 122.

FOR MONTH OF _____ 19____ PAGE ____

		5	6	7	8	9	10	
	ACCOUNTS RECEIVABLE		SALES CREDIT	ACCOUNTS PAYABLE		PURCHASES DEBIT	
	DEBIT	CREDIT		DEBIT	CREDIT		
1							1
2							2
3							3
4							4
5							5
6							6
7							7
8							8
9							9
10							10
11							11
12							12
13							13
14							14
15							15
16							16
17							17
18							18
19							19
20							20
21							21
22							22
23							23
24							24
25							25
26							26
27							27
28							28
29							29
30							30
31							31
32							32
33							33

Begin Mastery Problem 12-M on this page. The combination journal prepared here will be needed to complete Mastery Problem 13-M.

MASTERY PROBLEM 12-M, p. 193

COMBINATION JOURNAL

PAGE									
	1		2				3		4

	CASH			DATE	ACCOUNT TITLE	Doc. No.	Post. Ref.	GENERAL	
	DEBIT		CREDIT					DEBIT	CREDIT
1										1
2										2
3										3
4										4
5										5
6										6
7										7
8										8
9										9
10										10
11										11
12										12
13										13
14										14
15										15
16										16
17										17
18										18
19										19
20										20
21										21
22										22
23										23
24										24
25										25
26										26
27										27
28										28
29										29
30										30
31										31
32										32
33										33

Use this page with page 120.

FOR MONTH OF   19____   PAGE____

	ACCOUNTS RECEIVABLE		SALES CREDIT	ACCOUNTS PAYABLE		PURCHASES DEBIT	
	DEBIT	CREDIT		DEBIT	CREDIT		
1							1
2							2
3							3
4							4
5							5
6							6
7							7
8							8
9							9
10							10
11							11
12							12
13							13
14							14
15							15
16							16
17							17
18							18
19							19
20							20
21							21
22							22
23							23
24							24
25							25
26							26
27							27
28							28
29							29
30							30
31							31
32							32
33							33

COMBINATION JOURNAL

PAGE 1 2 3 4

| CASH | | DATE | ACCOUNT TITLE | DOC. NO. | POST. REF. | GENERAL | |
DEBIT	CREDIT					DEBIT	CREDIT

Keep the combination journal prepared for Mastery Problem 12-M in order to complete Mastery Problem 13-M in Chapter 13.

Name_____Date_____Class_____ *BONUS PROBLEM 12-B, concluded*

Begin this problem on pages 124 and 125. Use this page with page 126.

FOR MONTH OF _____ 19__ PAGE ____

| | ACCOUNTS PAYABLE | | ACCOUNTS RECEIVABLE | | PURCHASES DEBIT | SALES CREDIT | |
	DEBIT	CREDIT	DEBIT	CREDIT			
1							1
2							2
3							3
4							4
5							5
6							6
7							7
8							8
9							9
10							10
11							11
12							12
13							13
14							14
15							15
16							16
17							17
18							18
19							19
20							20
21							21
22							22
23							23
24							24
25							25
26							26
27							27
28							28
29							29
30							30
31							31
32							32
33							33

Begin Bonus Problem 12-B on this page. The combination journal prepared here will be needed to complete Bonus Problem 13-B.

BONUS PROBLEM 12-B, p. 194

PAGE _____

COMBINATION JOURNAL

	DATE		ACCOUNT TITLE	DOC. NO.	POST. REF.	GENERAL DEBIT	GENERAL CREDIT	CASH DEBIT	CASH CREDIT	
1										1
2										2
3										3
4										4
5										5
6										6
7										7
8										8
9										9
10										10
11										11
12										12
13										13
14										14
15										15
16										16
17										17
18										18
19										19
20										20
21										21
22										22
23										23
24										24
25										25
26										26
27										27
28										28
29										29
30										30
31										31
32										32
33										33

Use this page with page 124.

	FOR MONTH OF			19		PAGE	

	ACCOUNTS PAYABLE		ACCOUNTS RECEIVABLE		PURCHASES DEBIT	SALES CREDIT	
	DEBIT	CREDIT	DEBIT	CREDIT			
1							1
2							2
3							3
4							4
5							5
6							6
7							7
8							8
9							9
10							10
11							11
12							12
13							13
14							14
15							15
16							16
17							17
18							18
19							19
20							20
21							21
22							22
23							23
24							24
25							25
26							26
27							27
28							28
29							29
30							30
31							31
32							32
33							33

PAGE

COMBINATION JOURNAL

	DATE		ACCOUNT TITLE	DOC. NO.	POST. REF.	GENERAL		CASH		
						DEBIT	CREDIT	DEBIT	CREDIT	
1										1
2										2
3										3
4										4
5										5
6										6
7										7
8										8
9										9
10										10
11										11
12										12
13										13
14										14
15										15
16										16
17										17
18										18
19										19
20										20
21										21
22										22
23										23
24										24
25										25
26										26
27										27
28										28
29										29
30										30
31										31
32										32
33										33

Keep the combination journal prepared for Bonus Problem 12-B in order to complete Bonus Problem 13-B in Chapter 13.

Perfect Score..38

Deduct.......—

Your Score...—

Name_____

Date_____ Class_____

Checked by_____

Unit A—Business Vocabulary

DIRECTIONS: Complete each item in Column II by selecting one of the terms given in Column I. Then print the identifying letter of that term in the Answers column.

Column I

A — accounts payable
B — accounts payable ledger
C — accounts receivable
D — accounts receivable ledger
E — capital account
F — charge customer
G — controlling account
H — cycle billing
I — general ledger
J — purchase order
K — schedule of accounts payable
L — schedule of accounts receivable
M — statement of account
N — subsidiary ledger
O — work sheet

Column II

0. A list of customers that shows the balance due from each customer and the total amount due from all customers is called a...................

1. A list of all creditors that shows the balance owed to each creditor and the total amount owed to all creditors is called a.

2. A business form that shows the charges to a customer's account, the amounts credited to his account, and the balance of his account is called a.................

3. A ledger that contains all the accounts needed to prepare an income statement and a balance sheet is called a.........

4. A subsidiary ledger that contains accounts with creditors only is called an...................

5. An account in the general ledger that summarizes all the accounts in a subsidiary ledger is called a................

6. The general ledger account with a balance that equals the total of all the account balances in the accounts payable ledger is called.....................

7. A subsidiary ledger that contains accounts with charge customers only is called an...........................

8. A ledger that is summarized in a single account in the general ledger is called a.....................

9. A person or a business to whom a sale on account is made is called a...................

10. Preparing and mailing statements of account to customers on specific days of each month is called..................

	Answers	For Scoring
0.	L	0. ✓
1.		1.
2.		2.
3.		3.
4.		4.
5.		5.
6.		6.
7.		7.
8.		8.
9.		9.
10.		10.

Unit B—Examining the Combination Journal and the Ledgers

DIRECTIONS: After each statement given below, place a check mark (✓) in one of the Answers columns to indicate your answer.

0. The heading of a balance column of an account in the accounts receivable ledger is titled *Debit Balance*.................................

11. When the balance of a charge customer's account is changed, the balance of the controlling account, Accounts Receivable, must also be changed............

12. Each amount that is listed in the Accounts Receivable Debit column of the combination journal is posted individually to an account in the accounts receivable ledger.......................

13. Each amount that is listed in the Accounts Receivable Credit column of the combination journal is posted individually to an account in the general ledger....

14. Each amount that is listed in the General Credit column of the combination journal is posted individually as a credit to the account named in the Account Title column.....................

15. Each amount that is listed in the General Debit column of the combination journal is posted separately to some account in the accounts payable ledger...

16. Each cash payment to a creditor is posted as a credit to some account in the accounts payable ledger.......................

17. The sales account is the controlling account in the general ledger for the accounts receivable ledger.......................

18. The sum of the totals of all credit columns of the combination journal should equal the total of the Cash Debit column.......................

19. The cash on hand should be proved after the totals of the cash columns of the combination journal have been footed.......................

	Answers		For Scoring
	True	False	
0.	✓		0. ✓
11.			11.
12.			12.
13.			13.
14.			14.
15.			15.
16.			16.
17.			17.
18.			18.
19.			19.

DIRECTIONS: For each of the following items, select the answer that best completes the sentence. Then print in the Answers column at the right the capital letter identifying your choice.

	Answers	For Scoring

0. The total of the Cash Credit column of the combination journal is
   (A) not posted   **(B)** posted at the end of the month   **(C)** posted each day . . . . | *B* | 0. ✓ |

20. The total of the General Debit column of the combination journal is
   (A) not posted   **(B)** posted at the end of the month   **(C)** posted each day . . . . | | 20. |

21. The total of the Accounts Payable Debit column of the combination journal is
   (A) not posted   **(B)** posted at the end of the month   **(C)** posted each day . . . . | | 21. |

22. The individual amounts in the Sales Credit column of the combination journal are
   (A) posted only as a part of the column total   **(B)** posted separately each day
   (C) posted separately each week . . . . | | 22. |

23. The individual amounts in the General Debit column of the combination journal are
   (A) not posted   **(B)** posted only as part of the column total   **(C)** posted separately | | 23. |

24. The individual amounts in the Accounts Receivable Debit column of the combination journal are
   (A) not posted   **(B)** posted only as part of the column total   **(C)** posted separately | | 24. |

25. The accounts payable ledger form with balance-column ruling is desirable because it shows
   (A) at any time how much is owed to a creditor   **(B)** the name and address of each new creditor   **(C)** the account number of each creditor . . . . | | 25. |

26. Each account in the general ledger of Gift World has
   (A) two amount columns   **(B)** three amount columns   **(C)** four amount columns . . | | 26. |

27. The accounts receivable ledger contains an account for each
   (A) cash customer   **(B)** charge customer   **(C)** creditor . . . . | | 27. |

28. Gift World arranges the accounts in its accounts receivable ledger in
   (A) alphabetic order   **(B)** geographic order   **(C)** numeric order . . . . | | 28. |

29. Each entry in the Accounts Receivable Debit column of the combination journal is an amount that
   (A) has been collected from a charge customer   **(B)** has been paid to a creditor
   (C) is to be collected from a charge customer   **(D)** is to be paid to a creditor . . . . | | 29. |

30. Each entry in the Accounts Receivable Credit column of the combination journal is an amount that
   (A) has been collected from a charge customer   **(B)** has been paid to a creditor
   (C) is to be collected from a charge customer   **(D)** is to be paid to a creditor . . . . | | 30. |

31. The individual amounts from the Accounts Receivable Debit and Credit columns of the combination journal should be posted
   (A) daily   **(B)** weekly   **(C)** monthly . . . . | | 31. |

32. The accounts payable ledger contains an account for each
   (A) cash customer   **(B)** charge customer   **(C)** creditor . . . . | | 32. |

33. Gift World arranges the accounts in its accounts payable ledger in
   (A) alphabetic order   **(B)** geographic order   **(C)** numeric order . . . . | | 33. |

34. Each entry in the Accounts Payable Debit column of the combination journal is an amount that
   (A) has been collected from a charge customer   **(B)** has been paid to a creditor
   (C) is to be collected from a charge customer   **(D)** is to be paid to a creditor . . . . | | 34. |

35. Each entry in the Accounts Payable Credit column of the combination journal is an amount that
   (A) has been collected from a charge customer   **(B)** has been paid to a creditor
   (C) is to be collected from a charge customer   **(D)** is to be paid to a creditor . . . . | | 35. |

36. The individual amounts from the Accounts Payable Debit and Credit columns of the combination journal should be posted
   (A) daily   **(B)** weekly   **(C)** monthly . . . . | | 36. |

37. Each account in the general ledger is listed in the trial balance section of the work sheet
   (A) whether it has a balance or not   **(B)** only if it has a balance   **(C)** alphabetically . . | | 37. |

38. If all the posting is done correctly, the balance of a controlling account in the general ledger will equal
   (A) the net income for the fiscal period   **(B)** the sum of all of the charge customers' account balances   **(C)** the net loss for the fiscal period . . . . | | 38. |

Analyzing transactions of a merchandising business

1.   **Purchases**

325.00

           Accounts Payable

                          325.00

7.

2.

8.

3.

9.

4.

10.

5.

11.

6.

12.

The work completed for Drill 13-D 1 will be used to complete Drill 13-D 2.

[1]

Transaction	Amount columns in the combination journal									
	Cash		General		Accts. Rec.		Sales Credit	Accts. Pay.		Purchases Debit
	Debit	Credit	Debit	Credit	Debit	Credit		Debit	Credit	
1. Debit amount										✓
Credit amount									✓	
2. Debit amount										
Credit amount										
3. Debit amount										
Credit amount										
4. Debit amount										
Credit amount										
5. Debit amount										
Credit amount										
6. Debit amount										
Credit amount										
7. Debit amount										
Credit amount										
8. Debit amount										
Credit amount										
9. Debit amount										
Credit amount										
10. Debit amount										
Credit amount										
11. Debit amount										
Credit amount										
12. Debit amount										
Credit amount										

[2]

Transaction	Posted to			Not posted separately to any ledger
	General Ledger	Accounts Receivable Ledger	Accounts Payable Ledger	
1. Debit amount				✓
Credit amount			✓	
2. Debit amount				
Credit amount				
3. Debit amount				
Credit amount				
4. Debit amount				
Credit amount				
5. Debit amount				
Credit amount				
6. Debit amount				
Credit amount				
7. Debit amount				
Credit amount				
8. Debit amount				
Credit amount				
9. Debit amount				
Credit amount				
10. Debit amount				
Credit amount				
11. Debit amount				
Credit amount				
12. Debit amount				
Credit amount				

Begin Problem 13-1 on page 135.

[4]

[5]

PAGE 11   COMBINATION JOURNAL

	CASH		DATE	ACCOUNT TITLE	Doc. No.	Post. Ref.	GENERAL	
	DEBIT	CREDIT					DEBIT	CREDIT
1			Nov. 1	Balance on hand, $1,845.00		✓		
2		30000	1	Rent Expense	CK83		30000	
3	22500		2	Ben Hagar	R108			
4			3	Arlington, Inc.	P42			
5			4	Juanita Story	S76			
6		4000	5	Miscellaneous Expense	CK84		4000	
7	120000		5	✓	T5	✓		
8		22500	8	✓	CK85	✓		
9			9	Barry Taggart	S77			
10	30000		10	Harry Blackstone	R109			
11		90000	10	Jackson Supplies	CK86			
12			12	Supplies	M30		22500	
13				Suffolk Company				
14	108000		12	✓	T12	✓		
15		45000	15	Salary Expense	CK87		45000	
16	37500		16	Barry Taggart	R110			
17			17	Jackson Supplies	P43			
18			18	Ben Hagar	S78			
19	102000		19	✓	T19	✓		
20		16500	22	Arlington, Inc.	CK88			
21		3000	23	Miscellaneous Expense	CK89		3000	
22			24	Prepaid Insurance	M31		9000	
23				Supplies				9000
24			26	Juanita Story	S79			
25	111000		26	✓	T26	✓		
26		24000	29	✓	CK90	✓		
27		60000	30	Lyn Fisher, Drawing	CK91		60000	
28		12000	30	Delivery Expense	CK92		12000	
29		45000	30	Salary Expense	CK93		45000	
30		6000	30	Suffolk Company	CK94			
31	57000		30	✓	T30	✓		
32	588000	358000	30	Totals			230500	9000

FOR MONTH OF *November* 19 – –   PAGE *11*

	5	6	7	8	9	10	
	ACCOUNTS RECEIVABLE		SALES CREDIT	ACCOUNTS PAYABLE		PURCHASES DEBIT	
	DEBIT	CREDIT		DEBIT	CREDIT		
1							1
2							2
3		22500					3
4					27000	27000	4
5	6000		6000				5
6							6
7			120000				7
8						22500	8
9	4500		4500				9
10		30000					10
11				90000			11
12							12
13					22500		13
14			108000				14
15							15
16		37500					16
17					54000	54000	17
18	30000		30000				18
19			102000				19
20				16500			20
21							21
22							22
23							23
24	4500		4500				24
25			111000				25
26						24000	26
27							27
28							28
29							29
30				6000			30
31			57000				31
32	45000	90000	543000	112500	103500	127500	32
33							33

[7]

ACCOUNT TITLE	ACCT. NO.	TRIAL BALANCE		INCOME STATEMENT		BALANCE SHEET	
		1 DEBIT	2 CREDIT	3 DEBIT	4 CREDIT	5 DEBIT	6 CREDIT
1							
2							
3							
4							
5							
6							
7							
8							
9							
10							
11							
12							
13							
14							
15							
16							
17							
18							
19							
20							
21							
22							
23							
24							
25							

ACCOUNTS RECEIVABLE LEDGER

NAME *Harry Blackstone*

ADDRESS *1846 Camden Road, Dover, DE 19903*

DATE	ITEM	POST. REF.	DEBIT	CREDIT	DEBIT BALANCE
19-- Nov. 1	Balance	✓			30000

NAME *Ben Hagar*

ADDRESS *923 Laurel Avenue, Dover, DE 19901*

DATE	ITEM	POST. REF.	DEBIT	CREDIT	DEBIT BALANCE
19-- Nov. 1	Balance	✓			22500

NAME *Juanita Story*

ADDRESS *616 Mahon Boulevard, Dover, DE 19901*

DATE	ITEM	POST. REF.	DEBIT	CREDIT	DEBIT BALANCE

NAME *Barry Taggart*

ADDRESS *1042 Clayton Street, Dover, DE 19902*

DATE	ITEM	POST. REF.	DEBIT	CREDIT	DEBIT BALANCE
19-- Nov. 1	Balance	✓			37500

ACCOUNTS PAYABLE LEDGER

NAME *Arlington, Inc.*

ADDRESS *73846 Darby Boulevard, Philadelphia, PA 19143*

DATE	ITEM	POST. REF.	DEBIT	CREDIT	CREDIT BALANCE
19-- Nov. 1	Balance	✓			16500

NAME *Jackson Supplies*

ADDRESS *4652 Hartford Road, Baltimore, MD 21218*

DATE	ITEM	POST. REF.	DEBIT	CREDIT	CREDIT BALANCE
19-- Nov. 1	Balance	✓			90000

NAME *Suffolk Company*

ADDRESS *2834 Holland Road, Suffolk, VA 23434*

DATE	ITEM	POST. REF.	DEBIT	CREDIT	CREDIT BALANCE
19-- Nov. 1	Balance	✓			6000

NAME

ADDRESS

DATE	ITEM	POST. REF.	DEBIT	CREDIT	CREDIT BALANCE

GENERAL LEDGER

ACCOUNT *Cash*   ACCOUNT NO. *11*

DATE	ITEM	POST. REF.	DEBIT	CREDIT	BALANCE DEBIT	BALANCE CREDIT
19-- Nov. 1	Balance	✓			1845 00	

ACCOUNT *Accounts Receivable*   ACCOUNT NO. *12*

DATE	ITEM	POST. REF.	DEBIT	CREDIT	BALANCE DEBIT	BALANCE CREDIT
19-- Nov. 1	Balance	✓			900 00	

ACCOUNT *Merchandise Inventory*   ACCOUNT NO. *13*

DATE	ITEM	POST. REF.	DEBIT	CREDIT	BALANCE DEBIT	BALANCE CREDIT
19-- Nov. 1	Balance	✓			6180 00	

ACCOUNT *Supplies*   ACCOUNT NO. *14*

DATE	ITEM	POST. REF.	DEBIT	CREDIT	BALANCE DEBIT	BALANCE CREDIT
19-- Nov. 1	Balance	✓			180 00	

GENERAL LEDGER

ACCOUNT *Prepaid Insurance*   ACCOUNT NO. 15

DATE	ITEM	POST. REF.	DEBIT	CREDIT	BALANCE DEBIT	BALANCE CREDIT
19-- Nov. 1	Balance	✓			30000	

ACCOUNT *Accounts Payable*   ACCOUNT NO. 21

DATE	ITEM	POST. REF.	DEBIT	CREDIT	BALANCE DEBIT	BALANCE CREDIT
19-- Nov. 1	Balance	✓				112500

ACCOUNT *Lyn Fisher, Capital*   ACCOUNT NO. 31

DATE	ITEM	POST. REF.	DEBIT	CREDIT	BALANCE DEBIT	BALANCE CREDIT
19-- Nov. 1	Balance	✓				828000

ACCOUNT *Lyn Fisher, Drawing*   ACCOUNT NO. 32

DATE	ITEM	POST. REF.	DEBIT	CREDIT	BALANCE DEBIT	BALANCE CREDIT

GENERAL LEDGER

ACCOUNT *Income Summary* ACCOUNT NO. *33*

DATE	ITEM	POST. REF.	DEBIT	CREDIT	BALANCE DEBIT	BALANCE CREDIT

ACCOUNT *Sales* ACCOUNT NO. *41*

DATE	ITEM	POST. REF.	DEBIT	CREDIT	BALANCE DEBIT	BALANCE CREDIT

ACCOUNT *Purchases* ACCOUNT NO. *51*

DATE	ITEM	POST. REF.	DEBIT	CREDIT	BALANCE DEBIT	BALANCE CREDIT

ACCOUNT *Delivery Expense* ACCOUNT NO. *61*

DATE	ITEM	POST. REF.	DEBIT	CREDIT	BALANCE DEBIT	BALANCE CREDIT

GENERAL LEDGER

ACCOUNT *Insurance Expense*   ACCOUNT NO. 62

DATE	ITEM	POST. REF.	DEBIT	CREDIT	BALANCE	
					DEBIT	CREDIT

ACCOUNT *Miscellaneous Expense*   ACCOUNT NO. 63

DATE	ITEM	POST. REF.	DEBIT	CREDIT	BALANCE	
					DEBIT	CREDIT

ACCOUNT *Rent Expense*   ACCOUNT NO. 64

DATE	ITEM	POST. REF.	DEBIT	CREDIT	BALANCE	
					DEBIT	CREDIT

ACCOUNT *Salary Expense*   ACCOUNT NO. 65

DATE	ITEM	POST. REF.	DEBIT	CREDIT	BALANCE	
					DEBIT	CREDIT

ACCOUNT *Supplies Expense*   ACCOUNT NO. 66

DATE	ITEM	POST. REF.	DEBIT	CREDIT	BALANCE	
					DEBIT	CREDIT

Use the combination journal prepared in Mastery
Problem 12-M to complete Mastery Problem 13-M.

ACCOUNTS RECEIVABLE LEDGER

NAME Richard Hagen

ADDRESS 1346 Webster Street, Manchester, NH 03104

DATE	ITEM	POST. REF.	DEBIT	CREDIT	DEBIT BALANCE
19-- Nov. 1	Balance	✓			18000

NAME Glen Olsen

ADDRESS 6422 Kelley Street, Manchester, NH 03102

DATE	ITEM	POST. REF.	DEBIT	CREDIT	DEBIT BALANCE
19-- Nov. 1	Balance	✓			7500

NAME Alex Penner

ADDRESS 683 Boynton Street, Manchester, NH 03103

DATE	ITEM	POST. REF.	DEBIT	CREDIT	DEBIT BALANCE

NAME Joan Shelton

ADDRESS 2344 Hanover Street, Manchester, NH 03104

DATE	ITEM	POST. REF.	DEBIT	CREDIT	DEBIT BALANCE
19-- Nov. 1	Balance	✓			10500

ACCOUNTS PAYABLE LEDGER

NAME *Drake Supply*
ADDRESS *7840 Brighton Avenue, Portland, ME 04100*

DATE	ITEM	POST. REF.	DEBIT	CREDIT	CREDIT BALANCE
19-- Nov. 1	Balance	✓			9500

NAME *Masters Co.*
ADDRESS *3613 South Pine, Manchester, NH 03100*

DATE	ITEM	POST. REF.	DEBIT	CREDIT	CREDIT BALANCE

NAME *Ritz Paint Supplies*
ADDRESS *4972 Munroe Street, Boston, MA 02100*

DATE	ITEM	POST. REF.	DEBIT	CREDIT	CREDIT BALANCE
19-- Nov. 1	Balance	✓			12500

NAME *Soper, Inc.*
ADDRESS *1612 North Maple, Manchester, NH 03102*

DATE	ITEM	POST. REF.	DEBIT	CREDIT	CREDIT BALANCE
19-- Nov. 1	Balance	✓			6000

GENERAL LEDGER

ACCOUNT *Cash*   ACCOUNT NO. *11*

DATE	ITEM	POST. REF.	DEBIT	CREDIT	BALANCE DEBIT	BALANCE CREDIT
19-- Nov. 1	Balance	✓			170000	

ACCOUNT *Accounts Receivable*   ACCOUNT NO. *12*

DATE	ITEM	POST. REF.	DEBIT	CREDIT	BALANCE DEBIT	BALANCE CREDIT
19-- Nov. 1	Balance	✓			36000	

ACCOUNT *Merchandise Inventory*   ACCOUNT NO. *13*

DATE	ITEM	POST. REF.	DEBIT	CREDIT	BALANCE DEBIT	BALANCE CREDIT
19-- Nov. 1	Balance	✓			500000	

ACCOUNT *Supplies*   ACCOUNT NO. *14*

DATE	ITEM	POST. REF.	DEBIT	CREDIT	BALANCE DEBIT	BALANCE CREDIT
19-- Nov. 1	Balance	✓			7000	

GENERAL LEDGER

ACCOUNT *Prepaid Insurance*　　　　　　　　　ACCOUNT NO. 15

DATE	ITEM	POST. REF.	DEBIT	CREDIT	BALANCE	
					DEBIT	CREDIT
19-- Nov. 1	Balance	✓			100 00	

ACCOUNT *Accounts Payable*　　　　　　　　　ACCOUNT NO. 21

DATE	ITEM	POST. REF.	DEBIT	CREDIT	BALANCE	
					DEBIT	CREDIT
19-- Nov. 1	Balance	✓				280 00

ACCOUNT *Lee Coker, Capital*　　　　　　　　　ACCOUNT NO. 31

DATE	ITEM	POST. REF.	DEBIT	CREDIT	BALANCE	
					DEBIT	CREDIT
19-- Nov. 1	Balance	✓				6950 00

ACCOUNT *Lee Coker, Drawing*　　　　　　　　　ACCOUNT NO. 32

DATE	ITEM	POST. REF.	DEBIT	CREDIT	BALANCE	
					DEBIT	CREDIT

GENERAL LEDGER

ACCOUNT *Income Summary*   ACCOUNT NO. 33

DATE	ITEM	POST. REF.	DEBIT	CREDIT	BALANCE DEBIT	BALANCE CREDIT

ACCOUNT *Sales*   ACCOUNT NO. 41

DATE	ITEM	POST. REF.	DEBIT	CREDIT	BALANCE DEBIT	BALANCE CREDIT

ACCOUNT *Purchases*   ACCOUNT NO. 51

DATE	ITEM	POST. REF.	DEBIT	CREDIT	BALANCE DEBIT	BALANCE CREDIT

ACCOUNT *Delivery Expense*   ACCOUNT NO. 61

DATE	ITEM	POST. REF.	DEBIT	CREDIT	BALANCE DEBIT	BALANCE CREDIT

GENERAL LEDGER

ACCOUNT *Insurance Expense*   ACCOUNT NO. 62

DATE	ITEM	POST. REF.	DEBIT	CREDIT	BALANCE	
					DEBIT	CREDIT

ACCOUNT *Miscellaneous Expense*   ACCOUNT NO. 63

DATE	ITEM	POST. REF.	DEBIT	CREDIT	BALANCE	
					DEBIT	CREDIT

ACCOUNT *Rent Expense*   ACCOUNT NO. 64

DATE	ITEM	POST. REF.	DEBIT	CREDIT	BALANCE	
					DEBIT	CREDIT

ACCOUNT *Salary Expense*   ACCOUNT NO. 65

DATE	ITEM	POST. REF.	DEBIT	CREDIT	BALANCE	
					DEBIT	CREDIT

ACCOUNT *Supplies Expense*   ACCOUNT NO. 66

DATE	ITEM	POST. REF.	DEBIT	CREDIT	BALANCE	
					DEBIT	CREDIT

[4]

[6]

	ACCT. NO.	TRIAL BALANCE		INCOME STATEMENT		BALANCE SHEET	
ACCOUNT TITLE		1 DEBIT	2 CREDIT	3 DEBIT	4 CREDIT	5 DEBIT	6 CREDIT
1							
2							
3							
4							
5							
6							
7							
8							
9							
10							
11							
12							
13							
14							
15							
16							
17							
18							
19							
20							
21							
22							
23							
24							
25							

Use the combination journal prepared in Bonus
Problem 12-B to complete Bonus Problem 13-B.

ACCOUNTS RECEIVABLE LEDGER

NAME *Richard Hagen*

ADDRESS *1346 Webster Street, Manchester, NH 03104*

DATE	ITEM	POST. REF.	DEBIT	CREDIT	DEBIT BALANCE
19—— Nov. 1	Balance	✓			18000

NAME *Glen Olsen*

ADDRESS *6422 Kelley Street, Manchester, NH 03102*

DATE	ITEM	POST. REF.	DEBIT	CREDIT	DEBIT BALANCE
19—— Nov. 1	Balance	✓			7500

NAME *Alex Penner*

ADDRESS *683 Boynton Street, Manchester, NH 03103*

DATE	ITEM	POST. REF.	DEBIT	CREDIT	DEBIT BALANCE

NAME *Joan Shelton*

ADDRESS *2344 Hanover Street, Manchester, NH 03104*

DATE	ITEM	POST. REF.	DEBIT	CREDIT	DEBIT BALANCE
19—— Nov. 1	Balance	✓			10500

ACCOUNTS PAYABLE LEDGER

NAME *Drake Supply*

ADDRESS *7840 Brighton Avenue, Portland, ME 04100*

DATE	ITEM	POST. REF.	DEBIT	CREDIT	CREDIT BALANCE
19-- Nov. 1	Balance	✓			9500

NAME *Masters Co.*

ADDRESS *3613 South Pine, Manchester, NH 03100*

DATE	ITEM	POST. REF.	DEBIT	CREDIT	CREDIT BALANCE

NAME *Ritz Paint Supplies*

ADDRESS *4972 Munroe Street, Boston, MA 02100*

DATE	ITEM	POST. REF.	DEBIT	CREDIT	CREDIT BALANCE
19-- Nov. 1	Balance	✓			12500

NAME *Soper, Inc.*

ADDRESS *1612 North Maple, Manchester, NH 03102*

DATE	ITEM	POST. REF.	DEBIT	CREDIT	CREDIT BALANCE
19-- Nov. 1	Balance	✓			6000

GENERAL LEDGER

ACCOUNT *Cash*   ACCOUNT NO. *11*

DATE	ITEM	POST. REF.	DEBIT	CREDIT	BALANCE	
					DEBIT	CREDIT
19-- Nov. 1	Balance	✓			170000	

ACCOUNT *Accounts Receivable*   ACCOUNT NO. *12*

DATE	ITEM	POST. REF.	DEBIT	CREDIT	BALANCE	
					DEBIT	CREDIT
19-- Nov. 1	Balance	✓			36000	

ACCOUNT *Merchandise Inventory*   ACCOUNT NO. *13*

DATE	ITEM	POST. REF.	DEBIT	CREDIT	BALANCE	
					DEBIT	CREDIT
19-- Nov. 1	Balance	✓			500000	

ACCOUNT *Supplies*   ACCOUNT NO. *14*

DATE	ITEM	POST. REF.	DEBIT	CREDIT	BALANCE	
					DEBIT	CREDIT
19-- Nov. 1	Balance	✓			7000	

GENERAL LEDGER

ACCOUNT **Prepaid Insurance**　　　　　　　　ACCOUNT NO. 15

DATE	ITEM	POST. REF.	DEBIT	CREDIT	BALANCE DEBIT	BALANCE CREDIT
19-- Nov. 1	Balance	✓			10000	

ACCOUNT **Accounts Payable**　　　　　　　　ACCOUNT NO. 21

DATE	ITEM	POST. REF.	DEBIT	CREDIT	BALANCE DEBIT	BALANCE CREDIT
19-- Nov. 1	Balance	✓				28000

ACCOUNT **Lee Coker, Capital**　　　　　　　　ACCOUNT NO. 31

DATE	ITEM	POST. REF.	DEBIT	CREDIT	BALANCE DEBIT	BALANCE CREDIT
19-- Nov. 1	Balance	✓				695000

ACCOUNT **Lee Coker, Drawing**　　　　　　　　ACCOUNT NO. 32

DATE	ITEM	POST. REF.	DEBIT	CREDIT	BALANCE DEBIT	BALANCE CREDIT

GENERAL LEDGER

ACCOUNT *Income Summary*   ACCOUNT NO. *33*

DATE	ITEM	POST. REF.	DEBIT	CREDIT	BALANCE DEBIT	BALANCE CREDIT

ACCOUNT *Sales*   ACCOUNT NO. *41*

DATE	ITEM	POST. REF.	DEBIT	CREDIT	BALANCE DEBIT	BALANCE CREDIT

ACCOUNT *Purchases*   ACCOUNT NO. *51*

DATE	ITEM	POST. REF.	DEBIT	CREDIT	BALANCE DEBIT	BALANCE CREDIT

ACCOUNT *Delivery Expense*   ACCOUNT NO. *61*

DATE	ITEM	POST. REF.	DEBIT	CREDIT	BALANCE DEBIT	BALANCE CREDIT

GENERAL LEDGER

ACCOUNT *Insurance Expense*   ACCOUNT NO. 62

DATE	ITEM	POST. REF.	DEBIT	CREDIT	BALANCE DEBIT	BALANCE CREDIT

ACCOUNT *Miscellaneous Expense*   ACCOUNT NO. 63

DATE	ITEM	POST. REF.	DEBIT	CREDIT	BALANCE DEBIT	BALANCE CREDIT

ACCOUNT *Rent Expense*   ACCOUNT NO. 64

DATE	ITEM	POST. REF.	DEBIT	CREDIT	BALANCE DEBIT	BALANCE CREDIT

ACCOUNT *Salary Expense*   ACCOUNT NO. 65

DATE	ITEM	POST. REF.	DEBIT	CREDIT	BALANCE DEBIT	BALANCE CREDIT

ACCOUNT *Supplies Expense*   ACCOUNT NO. 66

DATE	ITEM	POST. REF.	DEBIT	CREDIT	BALANCE DEBIT	BALANCE CREDIT

[6]

ACCOUNT TITLE	ACCT. NO.	TRIAL BALANCE		INCOME STATEMENT		BALANCE SHEET	
		DEBIT	CREDIT	DEBIT	CREDIT	DEBIT	CREDIT
		1	2	3	4	5	6
1							
2							
3							
4							
5							
6							
7							
8							
9							
10							
11							
12							
13							
14							
15							
16							
17							
18							
19							
20							
21							
22							
23							
24							
25							

Perfect Score..47

Deduct.......—

Your Score...—

Name _____

Date _____ Class _____

Checked by _____

Unit A—Examining a Bank Statement

DIRECTIONS: In the partial bank statement illustrated at the right, each part is identified by a capital letter.

Answer each question given below the illustration by printing the appropriate capital letter in the Answers column.

VALLEY NATIONAL BANK
PHOENIX, ARIZONA 85000

STATEMENT OF ACCOUNT

A

ACCOUNT NUMBER	DATE OF STATEMENT
B	C

BALANCE FROM PREVIOUS STATEMENT	CHECKS	AMOUNT OF CHECKS	DEPOSITS	AMOUNT OF DEPOSITS	SERVICE CHARGE	STATEMENT BALANCE
D	E	F	G	H	I	J

DATE	CHECKS		CHECKS	DEPOSITS	BALANCE
K	L		M	N	O

Which capital letter or letters on the bank statement show the location of the:

	Answers	For Scoring
0. Depositor's account number?..........................	B	0. ✓
1. Name and address of the depositor?....................		1.
2. Day on which the bank statement is prepared?..........		2.
3. Day of the month on which each check is received by the bank?......		3.
4. Amount of each check paid by the bank?...............		4.
5. Depositor's balance at the beginning of the statement period?......		5.
6. Amount of each deposit?.............................		6.
7. Amount of the service charge?.......................		7.
8. Day of the month on which each deposit is received by the bank?.....		8.
9. Daily balance of the depositor's account?.............		9.
10. Depositor's balance at the end of the month?..........		10.
11. Total amount of all checks paid by the bank during the statement period............		11.

Unit B—Analyzing Bank Services

DIRECTIONS: After each statement given below, place a check mark (✓) in one of the Answers columns to indicate your answer.

	Answers True	Answers False	For Scoring
0. The deposit slip is sometimes known as a deposit ticket...................	✓		0. ✓
12. If the ABA number of a bank is *16-361*, the number assigned only to that bank is 361............... *1222*			12.
13. Checks may be listed on a deposit slip by the ABA number of the bank on which the check is drawn............			13.
14. A lost check with a special endorsement can be cashed by anyone who finds it..			14.
15. A stamped endorsement without a handwritten signature is unacceptable by most banks............			15.
16. A check that is written to the order of Joan Rost should be endorsed as Mrs. Joseph Rost............			16.
17. Gift World uses the check stub as the source document for journalizing a cash payment............			17.
18. Each time a bank deposit is made, the accounting clerk for Gift World records a debit to Cash in the combination journal............			18.
19. The memorandum entry that is made in the combination journal for a voided check includes a credit to Cash............			19.
20. The journal entry that is made in the combination journal to record a dishonored check includes a debit to Accounts Receivable............			20.
21. In reconciling a bank statement, the bank service charge should be added to the check-stub balance that is brought forward on the next unused check stub......			21.

DIRECTIONS: Complete each item in Column II by selecting the one term given in Column I that best completes the statement. Then print the identifying letter of that term in the Answers column.

		Answers	For Scoring

Column I

A — ABA numbers
B — bank balance
C — bank service charge
D — bank statement
E — blank endorsement
F — canceled checks
G — check
H — checking account
I — depositor
J — deposit slip
K — dishonored check
L — drawee
M — drawer
N — endorsement
O — magnetic ink characters
P — making a deposit
Q — MICR
R — outstanding checks
S — outstanding deposit
T — payee
U — payer
V — qualified endorsement
W — reconciling the bank statement
X — restrictive endorsement
Y — savings account
Z — signature card
AA — special endorsement
BB — statement of account
CC — voiding a check
DD — withdrawals

Column II

0. An order in writing, signed by the depositor, ordering the bank to pay cash from the depositor's account to a person or business named is called a . . . .   **G**   0. ✓

22. Checks that have been paid by the bank and returned to the depositor with the bank statement are called . . . .   22.

23. Special number characters printed in magnetic ink that can be "read" by automatic machines are called . . . .   23.

24. Placing cash in a bank is called . . . .   24.

25. The business form provided by the bank on which a depositor lists all cash and checks to be deposited is called a . . . .   25.

26. An endorsement that consists only of the name of the endorser is called a . . . .   26.

27. Writing the word *Void* across the face of a check and the stub to indicate that the check and stub are not to be used is called . . . .   27.

28. The bank on which the check is drawn is called the . . . .   28.

29. The ending balance that appears on the depositor's ledger account is called the . . . .   29.

30. The person or business in whose name cash is deposited is called a . . . .   30.

31. An abbreviation commonly used for magnetic ink character recognition is . . . .   31.

32. The person who signs the check ordering the bank to pay cash from that person's account or the account of the business is called the . . . .   32.

33. Checks that have been issued but not yet cashed at the bank are called . . . .   33.

34. An account with a bank from which a depositor can order payments to others is called a . . . .   34.

35. A deposit that has been made, but which is not shown on the bank statement, is called an . . . .   35.

36. A check that the bank refuses to pay is called a . . . .   36.

37. An endorsement that restricts further transfers of the check is called a . . . .   37.

38. An account with a bank on which the bank pays interest to the depositor is called a . . . .   38.

39. An endorsement that states to whom the check is to be paid, followed by the name of the endorser is called a . . . .   39.

40. The signature or stamp of the depositor on the back of a check authorizing transfer of ownership is called an . . . . . .   40.

41. The report the bank sends to a depositor showing the deposits, the withdrawals, and the ending bank balance is called a . . . .   41.

42. Identification numbers assigned to banks by the American Bankers Association are called . .   42.

43. The person or business to whom the bank is ordered to pay the cash is called the . . . .   43.

44. The process of bringing the bank balance and the check-stub balance into agreement is called . . . .   44.

45. A charge made by a bank for maintaining a checking account is called a . . . .   45.

46. A form signed by each individual authorized to sign checks on a checking account is called   46.

47. An endorsement in which the endorser does not accept any responsibility for payment on the check is called a . . . .   47.

Reconciling a bank statement

Reconciling a bank statement   *DRILL 14-D 2, p. 234*

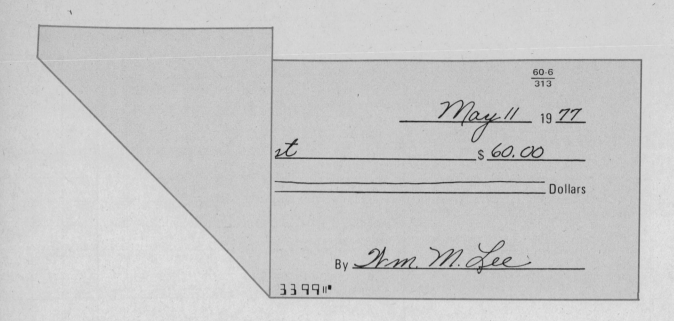

$\dfrac{60\text{-}6}{313}$

_____ May 11 __ 19 77

it _____ $ 60.00 _____

_____ Dollars

By *Wm. M. Lee* _____

3399

Preparing a deposit slip

**CITIZENS
STATE
BANK
MEDFORD, OR 97501**

$\dfrac{96\text{-}315}{1232}$

For deposit to the account of

EUGENIA YOUNG
101 Walnut Lane
Medford, OR 97501

Date _____ 19 ____		
Cash		
Checks		
TOTAL		

1232 0315 148 64530

Writing checks and recording a deposit in the checkbook

No.____ Date ____ 19___$_____

To_____

_____

For_____

BAL. BRO'T. FOR'D.

AMT. DEPOSITED

TOTAL

AMT. THIS CHECK

BAL. CAR'D. FOR'D.

		19		
		DATE		

DALE PATTON
220 ABERDEEN
HARRISBURG, PA. 17101

No._____

64-515
313

19_____

Pay to the
order of _____ $_____

_____ Dollars

DALE PATTON

PEOPLES BANK OF HARRISBURG

Harrisburg, Pennsylvania 17101

⑆313⑈515⑆   162⑈0017⑈04⑈

No.____ Date ____ 19___$_____

To_____

_____

For_____

BAL. BRO'T. FOR'D.

AMT. DEPOSITED

TOTAL

AMT. THIS CHECK

BAL. CAR'D. FOR'D.

		19		
		DATE		

DALE PATTON
220 ABERDEEN
HARRISBURG, PA. 17101

No._____

64-515
313

19_____

Pay to the
order of _____ $_____

_____ Dollars

DALE PATTON

PEOPLES BANK OF HARRISBURG

Harrisburg, Pennsylvania 17101

⑆313⑈515⑆   162⑈0017⑈04⑈

No.____ Date ____ 19___$_____

To_____

_____

For_____

BAL. BRO'T. FOR'D.

AMT. DEPOSITED

TOTAL

AMT. THIS CHECK

BAL. CAR'D. FOR'D.

		19		
		DATE		

DALE PATTON
220 ABERDEEN
HARRISBURG, PA. 17101

No._____

64-515
313

19_____

Pay to the
order of _____ $_____

_____ Dollars

DALE PATTON

PEOPLES BANK OF HARRISBURG

Harrisburg, Pennsylvania 17101

⑆313⑈515⑆   162⑈0017⑈04⑈

[1]

[2]

COMBINATION JOURNAL

PAGE											
1	2				3	4			5	6	
CASH		DATE	ACCOUNT TITLE	Doc. No.	Post. Ref.	GENERAL			ACCOUNTS RECEIVABLE		
DEBIT	CREDIT					DEBIT	CREDIT		DEBIT	CREDIT	
								1			
								2			
								3			
								4			
								5			
								6			
								7			
								8			
								9			
								10			
								11			

Perfect Score..56

Deduct.......—

Your Score...—

Name _____

Date _____ Class _____

Checked by _____

STUDY GUIDE

15

Unit A—Format of the Eight-Column Work Sheet

DIRECTIONS: Each part and column of the eight-column work sheet form illustrated below is identified by a capital letter. Answer each question below the illustration by printing the appropriate capital letter in the Answers column.

		H						
		I						
		J						
A	B	C DEBIT / CREDIT		D DEBIT / CREDIT		E DEBIT / CREDIT		F DEBIT / CREDIT
G								

Which capital letter on the work sheet represents the position for writing the heading for the:

	Answers	For Scoring
0. ACCT. NO.?................	B	0. √
1. ADJUSTMENTS?..............		1.
2. BALANCE SHEET?............		2.
3. ACCOUNT TITLE?............		3.
4. TRIAL BALANCE?............		4.
5. INCOME STATEMENT?.........		5.

Which capital letter on the work sheet represents the position for writing the:

	Answers	For Scoring
6. Name of the business?........		6.
7. Date for which the work sheet is prepared?..............		7.
8. Words *Work Sheet*?...........		8.
9. Length of the fiscal period?...		9.

Unit B—The Nature of Account Balances

DIRECTIONS: After each account title given below in alphabetic order, place a check mark in the proper Trial Balance Debit or Credit column to indicate where its account balance should appear. Place a zero in both columns if the account does not have an amount in either column.

	Trial Balance Debit	Credit	For Scoring
0. Accounts Payable.........		√	0. √
10. Accounts Receivable......			10.
11. Cash....................			11.
12. Debra Horn, Capital......			12.
13. Debra Horn, Drawing.....			13.
14. Delivery Expense........			14.
15. Income Summary........			15.
16. Insurance Expense........			16.
17. Merchandise Inventory....			17.
18. Miscellaneous Expense....			18.
19. Prepaid Insurance........			19.
20. Purchases...............			20.
21. Rent Expense............			21.
22. Salary Expense...........			22.
23. Sales...................			23.
24. Supplies................			24.
25. Supplies Expense.........			25.

Unit C—Extensions on the Eight-Column Work Sheet

DIRECTIONS: After each account title given below, place a check mark in the column to which the account balance would be extended on the work sheet.

	Income Statement Debit	Credit	Balance Sheet Debit	Credit	For Scoring
0. Cash.............			√		0. √
26. Accts. Receivable..					26.
27. Mdse. Inventory...					27.
28. Supplies..........					28.
29. Prepaid Insurance.					29.
30. Accounts Payable..					30.
31. Debra Horn, Capital..........					31.
32. Debra Horn, Drawing.........					32.
33. Income Summary.					33.
34. Sales.............					34.
35. Purchases.........					35.
36. Delivery Expense..					36.
37. Insurance Expense.					37.
38. Misc. Expense....					38.
39. Rent Expense.....					39.
40. Salary Expense....					40.
41. Supplies Expense..					41.

DIRECTIONS: For each of the following items, select the answer that best completes the sentence. Then print in the Answers column at the right the capital letter identifying your choice.

	Answers	For Scoring

0. Items that should be extended to the Income Statement columns of the work sheet are **(A)** assets **(B)** liabilities **(C)** capital **(D)** expenses.......................... | *D* | 0. ✓

42. Account titles are listed on the work sheet **(A)** in alphabetic order **(B)** with income statement accounts first **(C)** in the order in which they appear in the general ledger **(D)** with the shortest names first...................................... | | 42.

43. On the line for Merchandise Inventory on the work sheet, the amount in the Trial Balance Debit column represents the value of merchandise **(A)** purchased during the fiscal period **(B)** at the beginning of the fiscal period **(C)** sold during the fiscal period **(D)** at the end of the fiscal period................. | | 43.

44. To compute cost of merchandise sold, to purchases **(A)** add beginning merchandise inventory and subtract ending merchandise inventory **(B)** subtract beginning and add ending merchandise inventory **(C)** add both beginning and ending merchandise inventory **(D)** subtract both beginning and ending merchandise inventory......... | | 44.

45. On the line for the asset account Supplies on the work sheet, the amount in the Trial Balance Debit column represents the cost of supplies **(A)** at the beginning of the fiscal period **(B)** bought during the fiscal period **(C)** used during the fiscal period **(D)** available during the fiscal period.............. | | 45.

46. The two accounts used in making the adjustment for supplies are **(A)** Merchandise Inventory and Supplies **(B)** Income Summary and Supplies Expense **(C)** Income Summary and Supplies **(D)** Supplies and Supplies Expense............. | | 46.

47. Supplies used during the fiscal period are classified as **(A)** an asset **(B)** a liability **(C)** an expense **(D)** capital.................... | | 47.

48. The portion of the insurance premiums that has expired, or has been used up, during the fiscal period of a business is classified as **(A)** an asset **(B)** an expense **(C)** a liability **(D)** capital.................... | | 48.

49. The two accounts used in making the adjustment for expired insurance are **(A)** Prepaid Insurance and Income Summary **(B)** Prepaid Insurance and Insurance Expense **(C)** Income Summary and Insurance Expense **(D)** Merchandise Inventory and Prepaid Insurance................ | | 49.

50. On the line for Prepaid Insurance on the work sheet, the amount in the Trial Balance Debit column represents the value of insurance premiums **(A)** at the beginning of the fiscal period plus premiums paid during the fiscal period **(B)** paid during the fiscal period **(C)** expired during the fiscal period **(D)** at the end of the fiscal period.................... | | 50.

51. On the line for Merchandise Inventory on the work sheet, the amount extended to the Balance Sheet Debit column represents the value of merchandise **(A)** on hand at the beginning of the fiscal period **(B)** purchased during the fiscal period **(C)** sold during the fiscal period **(D)** on hand at the end of the fiscal period.......... | | 51.

52. On the line for Supplies Expense on the work sheet, the amount extended to the Income Statement Debit column represents the value of supplies **(A)** bought during the fiscal period **(B)** available during the fiscal period **(C)** used during the fiscal period **(D)** at the end of the fiscal period................ | | 52.

53. On the line for Prepaid Insurance on the work sheet, the amount extended to the Balance Sheet Debit column represents the value of insurance premiums **(A)** at the beginning of the fiscal period **(B)** at the end of the fiscal period **(C)** expired during the fiscal period **(D)** paid during the fiscal period.............. | | 53.

54. On the line for Income Summary on the work sheet, the amount in the Adjustments Debit column represents the value of the **(A)** beginning merchandise inventory **(B)** purchases for the fiscal period **(C)** sales for the fiscal period **(D)** ending merchandise inventory.................... | | 54.

55. On the line for Income Summary on the work sheet, the amount in the Adjustments Credit column represents the value of the **(A)** beginning merchandise inventory **(B)** purchases for the fiscal period **(C)** sales for the fiscal period **(D)** ending merchandise inventory.................... | | 55.

56. Adjustments are posted to the general ledger accounts from the **(A)** Adjustments column of the work sheet **(B)** adjusting entries **(C)** previous month's ledger accounts **(D)** income summary account............... | | 56.

Adjusting the merchandise inventory account

Record the adjustments on the partial work sheets given below.

		ACCT. No.	ACCOUNT TITLE	TRIAL BALANCE DEBIT	TRIAL BALANCE CREDIT	ADJUSTMENTS DEBIT	ADJUSTMENTS CREDIT
				1	2	3	4
Business Firm A	3	Merchandise Inventory		7 8 4 0 00			
	9	Income Summary					
Business Firm B	3	Merchandise Inventory		———			
	9	Income Summary					
Business Firm C	3	Merchandise Inventory		10 6 4 0 00			
	9	Income Summary					
Business Firm D	3	Merchandise Inventory		2 3 9 2 00			
	9	Income Summary					

Adjusting the supplies and prepaid insurance accounts   *DRILL 15-D 2, p. 263*

Use the partial work sheets given below to record the adjustments and to extend the amounts to the Balance Sheet columns. Then complete the form at the bottom of the page.

ACCOUNT TITLE	TRIAL BALANCE DEBIT	TRIAL BALANCE CREDIT	ADJUSTMENTS DEBIT	ADJUSTMENTS CREDIT	BALANCE SHEET DEBIT	BALANCE SHEET CREDIT
	1	2	3	4	7	8
Business Firm A						
Supplies	3 6 0 00					
Prepaid Insurance	4 8 0 00					
Business Firm B						
Supplies	8 1 0 00					
Prepaid Insurance	6 0 00					

Business Firm	Account	(a) Amount of adjustment needed to update account	(b) & (c) Adjustments column in which amount is recorded to show the change in account	(d) and (e) Balance of account that is extended to Balance Sheet Debit column
A	Supplies.............	_____	_____	_____
	Prepaid Insurance.....	_____	_____	_____
B	Supplies.............	_____	_____	_____
	Prepaid Insurance.....	_____	_____	_____

Extensions on the work sheet [1-4]

A. L. Jurgens Company

Work Sheet

For Month Ended April 30, 19—

ACCT. NO.	ACCOUNT TITLE	TRIAL BALANCE		ADJUSTMENTS		INCOME STATEMENT		BALANCE SHEET	
		1 DEBIT	2 CREDIT	3 DEBIT	4 CREDIT	5 DEBIT	6 CREDIT	7 DEBIT	8 CREDIT
1									
2									
3									
4									
5									
6									
7									
8									
9									
10									
11									
12									
13									
14									
15									
16									
17									
18									
19									
20									
21									
22									
23									
24									
25									

Work sheet for an appliance store

Problem 15-1 work sheet is required for Problem 16-1. Your teacher will return this work sheet to you before it is needed in Problem 16-1.

ACCOUNT TITLE	ACCT. NO.	TRIAL BALANCE		ADJUSTMENTS		INCOME STATEMENT		BALANCE SHEET	
		1 DEBIT	2 CREDIT	3 DEBIT	4 CREDIT	5 DEBIT	6 CREDIT	7 DEBIT	8 CREDIT
1									
2									
3									
4									
5									
6									
7									
8									
9									
10									
11									
12									
13									
14									
15									
16									
17									
18									
19									
20									
21									
22									
23									
24									
25									

ACCOUNT TITLE	ACCT. NO.	TRIAL BALANCE		ADJUSTMENTS		INCOME STATEMENT		BALANCE SHEET	
		1 DEBIT	2 CREDIT	3 DEBIT	4 CREDIT	5 DEBIT	6 CREDIT	7 DEBIT	8 CREDIT
1									
2									
3									
4									
5									
6									
7									
8									
9									
10									
11									
12									
13									
14									
15									
16									
17									
18									
19									
20									
21									
22									
23									
24									
25									

Work sheet for a hardware store

	ACCT. NO.	TRIAL BALANCE		ADJUSTMENTS		INCOME STATEMENT		BALANCE SHEET	
ACCOUNT TITLE		DEBIT	CREDIT	DEBIT	CREDIT	DEBIT	CREDIT	DEBIT	CREDIT
		1	2	3	4	5	6	7	8
1									
2									
3									
4									
5									
6									
7									
8									
9									
10									
11									
12									
13									
14									
15									
16									
17									
18									
19									
20									
21									
22									
23									
24									
25									

Work sheet for a florist shop

		1	2	3	4	5	6	7	8
ACCOUNT TITLE	ACCT. NO.	TRIAL BALANCE		ADJUSTMENTS		INCOME STATEMENT		BALANCE SHEET	
		DEBIT	CREDIT	DEBIT	CREDIT	DEBIT	CREDIT	DEBIT	CREDIT
1									
2									
3									
4									
5									
6									
7									
8									
9									
10									
11									
12									
13									
14									
15									
16									
17									
18									
19									
20									
21									
22									
23									
24									
25									

Perfect Score..50

Deduct.......—

Your Score...—

Name _____

Date _____ Class _____

Checked by _____

Unit A—Business Vocabulary

DIRECTIONS: Complete each item in Column II by selecting one of the terms given in Column I. Then print the identifying letter of that term in the Answers column.

Column I

A — account form of balance sheet

B — accrual basis of accounting

C — capital statement

D — cash basis of accounting

E — cost of merchandise sold

F — gross profit on sales

G — net income

H — net loss

I — report form of balance sheet

J — supporting schedule

K — work sheet

Column II

	Column II	Answers	For Scoring
0.	A balance sheet with the assets listed on the left-hand side and the liabilities and capital listed on the right side is called the............	*A*	0. ✓
1.	A financial statement that summarizes the changes in capital during a fiscal period is called a.........................		1.
2.	A report prepared to give details about an item on a principal financial statement is called a.........		2.
3.	When the expenses of a business are greater than the gross profit on sales, the difference is called..................		3.
4.	The method of accounting that includes (1) all revenue earned during a fiscal period and (2) all expenses incurred during the fiscal period is called the.......................		4.
5.	A balance sheet with the assets, liabilities, and capital listed in a vertical arrangement is called the.................		5.
6.	The revenue that a merchandising business earns from operations before expenses are deducted is called.........		6.
7.	The method of accounting that includes (1) only revenue actually received during a fiscal period and (2) only expenses paid during a fiscal period is called the.................		7.

Unit B—Classifying Accounts

DIRECTIONS: Identify the group to which each account title listed below belongs by printing in the Answers column the capital letter (or letters) of the following code.

A — Assets
N — Not an account
C — Capital
L — Liabilities
E — Expense
R — Revenue
CM — Cost of Merchandise

		Answers	For Scoring
0.	Miscellaneous Expense......	*E*	0. ✓
8.	Accounts Payable..........		8.
9.	Accounts Receivable.......		9.
10.	Cash....................		10.
11.	Debra Horn, Capital.......		11.
12.	Debra Horn, Drawing......		12.
13.	Delivery Expense..........		13.
14.	Gross Profit..............		14.
15.	Income Summary..........		15.
16.	Insurance Expense........		16.

		Answers	For Scoring
17.	Merchandise Inventory.....		17.
18.	Net Income...............		18.
19.	Prepaid Insurance..........		19.
20.	Purchases................		20.
21.	Rent Expense.............		21.
22.	Salary Expense...........		22.
23.	Sales....................		23.
24.	Supplies.................		24.
25.	Supplies Expense..........		25.

Unit C—Examining Financial Statements for a Merchandising Business

DIRECTIONS: After each statement given below, place a check mark (√) in one of the Answers columns to indicate your answer.

	Answers		For Scoring
	True	False	
0. The income statement for a merchandising business has three main sections.....	√		0. √
26. A primary purpose for keeping financial records is to report the financial progress and condition of a business..............			26.
27. The data for the revenue section of the income statement are obtained from the Income Statement Debit column of the work sheet...........			27.
28. The data for the cost of merchandise sold section of the income statement are obtained from the Trial Balance columns of the work sheet............			28.
29. The cost of merchandise sold is determined by adding the value of the ending merchandise inventory to the amount of the purchases for the fiscal period........			29.
30. The data for the expenses section of the income statement are obtained from the Income Statement Debit column of the work sheet...........			30.
31. The total of the expenses on the income statement is deducted from the cost of merchandise sold to find the net income...........			31.
32. If the gross profit on sales is greater than total expenses, the difference is called net income.............			32.
33. Revenue less cost of merchandise sold equals net income.............			33.
34. If the debit side of the Income Statement columns on a work sheet is greater than the credit side, a net loss has been incurred...........			34.
35. The data needed to prepare a capital statement are taken from the capital account in the general ledger and from the Income Statement columns of the work sheet..........			35.
36. In preparing a capital statement, the data obtained from the work sheet include (1) the amount of withdrawals during the fiscal period and (2) the amount of net income or net loss for the fiscal period..........			36.
37. An additional investment of money in the business by the proprietor during a fiscal period affects the capital of that business...........			37.
38. Changes in the amount of capital occur when the business uses cash to purchase new equipment...........			38.
39. The information on the capital statement may be included as part of the income statement...........			39.
40. The capital of a business is affected when the business earns a profit or incurs a loss from its operation...........			40.
41. A net decrease in capital occurs when the net income for the fiscal period is greater than the withdrawals of cash and merchandise by the proprietor........			41.
42. The data needed to prepare the assets section of the balance sheet are obtained from the Balance Sheet Credit column of the work sheet...........			42.
43. The data needed to prepare the liabilities section of the balance sheet are obtained from the Balance Sheet Credit column of the work sheet............			43.
44. If the total amount of assets and the total amount of revenue and capital on a balance sheet are the same, the balance sheet is assumed to be correct.........			44.
45. Net income is shown on the bottom line of a balance sheet............			45.
46. A supporting schedule is sometimes known as a financial statement that reports changes in capital...........			46.
47. The total of the amounts listed on the Schedule of Accounts Receivable should be the same as the balance of the Accounts Receivable account in the general ledger...........			47.
48. The filing of income tax returns either on the accrual basis or the cash basis of keeping records is permitted by federal and state income tax laws...........			48.
49. Most of the information needed for filling out Schedule C, Form 1040, a section of the Federal income tax return, is on the balance sheet of the business........			49.
50. The terms *net profit* and *net income* are never used interchangeably...........			50.

Figuring the cost of merchandise sold

WORK SHEET DATA	Income Statement		Cost of Merchandise Sold
	Debit	Credit	
Business 1:			
Purchases..	$ 6,768.00		
Income Summary.....................................	7,320.00	$5,880.00	————
Business 2:			
Purchases..	$14,400.00		
Income Summary.....................................	15,724.00	....	————
Business 3:			
Purchases..	$10,030.00		
Income Summary.....................................	....	7,322.00	————

Drill 16-D 2 is on page 174.

Figuring the present capital

DATA FROM WORK SHEETS AND THE OWNER'S CAPITAL ACCOUNTS	Business 1	Business 2	Business 3	Business 4
Beginning capital...........................	$14,880.00	$ 8,940.00	$10,260.00	$12,600.00
Net income.................................	3,120.00	1,800.00	......	......
Net loss...................................	......	......	550.00	1,920.00
Additional investment......................	......	......	2,400.00	1,200.00
Withdrawals...............................	......	540.00	......	240.00
Current capital............................	————	————	————	————

Figuring the net income or net loss

WORK SHEET DATA	Income Statement		(a) Cost of Merchandise Sold	(b) Gross Profit on Sales	(c) Net Income (+) or Net Loss (−)
	Debit	Credit			
Business 1:					
Income Summary	$6,000.00	$3,600.00			
Sales		9,000.00			
Purchases	4,200.00				
Total Expenses	840.00				
Business 2:					
Income Summary	$9,600.00	$4,800.00			
Sales		10,800.00			
Purchases	4,800.00				
Total Expenses	1,200.00				
Business 3:					
Income Summary	$1,800.00	$2,400.00			
Sales		9,600.00			
Purchases	8,880.00				
Total Expenses	2,040.00				

Financial reports for an appliance store (net income; no additional investment)

Problem 15-1 work sheet is required for Problem 16-1. If it has not been returned to you, complete Review Problem 16-R 1.

[2]

[3]

Federal income tax returns for an
appliance store

SCHEDULE C
(Form 1040)
Department of the Treasury
Internal Revenue Service

Profit or (Loss) From Business or Profession
(Sole Proprietorship)
Partnerships, Joint Ventures, etc., Must File Form 1065.
► Attach to Form 1040.   ► See Instructions for Schedule C (Form 1040).

1977

C

Name(s) as shown on Form 1040	Social security number
D. R. Whitley	234 41 6839

A Principal business activity (see Schedule C Instructions) ► *Retail* ; product ► *Appliances*

B Business name ► *Whitley Appliances*   C Employer identification number ► *78-7825618*

D Business address (number and street) ► *3314 North Meridian Street*

City, State and ZIP code ► *Indianapolis, IN 46208*

E Indicate method of accounting: (1) ☐ Cash (2) ☒ Accrual (3) ☐ Other ►

	Yes	No
F Were you required to file Form W-3 or Form 1096 for 1977? (see Schedule C Instructions)		X
If "Yes," where filed ►		
G Was an Employer's Quarterly Federal Tax Return, Form 941, filed for this business for any quarter in 1977?	X	
H Method of inventory valuation ► *First in, first out* Was there any substantial change in the manner of determining quantities, costs, or valuations between the opening and closing inventories? (If "Yes," attach explanation)		X

Income

1 Gross receipts or sales $ _____ Less: returns and allowances $ _____ Balance ►	1	
2 Less: Cost of goods sold and/or operations (Schedule C-1, line 8)	2	
3 Gross profit	3	
4 Other income (attach schedule)	4	
5 **Total income** (add lines 3 and 4)	5	

Deductions

6 Depreciation (explain in Schedule C-3)	6	
7 Taxes on business and business property (explain in Schedule C-2)	7	
8 Rent on business property	8	
9 Repairs (explain in Schedule C-2)	9	
10 Salaries and wages not included on line 3, Schedule C-1 (exclude any paid to yourself)	10	
11 Insurance	11	
12 Legal and professional fees	12	
13 Commissions	13	
14 Amortization (attach statement)	14	
15 (a) Pension and profit-sharing plans (see Schedule C Instructions)	15(a)	
(b) Employee benefit programs (see Schedule C Instructions)	(b)	
16 Interest on business indebtedness	16	
17 Bad debts arising from sales or services	17	
18 Depletion	18	
19 Other business expenses (specify):		
(a)		
(b)		
(c)		
(d)		
(e)		
(f)		
(g)		
(h)		
(i)		
(j)		
(k) Total other business expenses (add lines 19(a) through 19(j))	19(k)	
20 **Total deductions** (add lines 6 through 19(k))	20	
21 Net profit or (loss) (subtract line 20 from line 5). Enter here and on Form 1040, line 28. **ALSO** enter on Schedule SE, line 5(a)	21	

SCHEDULE C-1.—Cost of Goods Sold and/or Operations (See Schedule C Instructions for Line 2)

1 Inventory at beginning of year (if different from last year's closing inventory, attach explanation)	1	
2 Purchases $ _____ Less: cost of items withdrawn for personal use $ _____ Balance ►	2	
3 Cost of labor (do not include salary paid to yourself)	3	
4 Materials and supplies	4	
5 Other costs (attach schedule)	5	
6 Total of lines 1 through 5	6	
7 Less: Inventory at end of year	7	
8 Cost of goods sold and/or operations. Enter here and on line 2 above	8	

Work sheet for a furniture store (net loss; additional investment)   [1]

ACCOUNT TITLE	ACCT. NO.	TRIAL BALANCE		ADJUSTMENTS		INCOME STATEMENT		BALANCE SHEET	
		1 DEBIT	2 CREDIT	3 DEBIT	4 CREDIT	5 DEBIT	6 CREDIT	7 DEBIT	8 CREDIT
1									
2									
3									
4									
5									
6									
7									
8									
9									
10									
11									
12									
13									
14									
15									
16									
17									
18									
19									
20									
21									
22									
23									
24									
25									

Financial statements for a furniture store
(net loss; additional investment)

[4]

Name_____Date_____Class_____

Work sheet for an auto supply store (net income; additional investment)   [1]

	ACCT. NO.	TRIAL BALANCE		ADJUSTMENTS		INCOME STATEMENT		BALANCE SHEET	
ACCOUNT TITLE		DEBIT	CREDIT	DEBIT	CREDIT	DEBIT	CREDIT	DEBIT	CREDIT
		1	2	3	4	5	6	7	8
1									
2									
3									
4									
5									
6									
7									
8									
9									
10									
11									
12									
13									
14									
15									
16									
17									
18									
19									
20									
21									
22									
23									
24									
25									

Financial statements for an auto supply store
(net income; additional investment)

[4]

Perfect Score..48

Deduct......—

Your Score...—

Name _____

Date _____ Class _____

Checked by _____

Unit A—Analyzing Adjusting Entries and Closing Entries

DIRECTIONS: For each transaction given below, print in the appropriate Answers column the identifying capital letters of the accounts to be debited and credited. Select the capital letters from the account titles listed at the left.

A — Allen Bale, Capital
B — Allen Bale, Drawing
C — Income Summary
D — Insurance Expense
E — Merchandise Inventory
F — Prepaid Insurance
G — Purchases
H — Sales
I — Supplies
J — Supplies Expense

		Answers		For Scoring	
		Debit	Credit	Debit	Credit
0-0.	Make the adjustment for beginning merchandise inventory.............	C	E	0. √	0. √
1-2.	Record the ending merchandise inventory.....................			1.	2.
3-4.	Adjust the supplies account...........			3.	4.
5-6.	Adjust the prepaid insurance account...			5.	6.
7-8.	Close the sales account..............			7.	8.
9-10.	Close the purchases account..........			9.	10.
11-12.	Close the insurance expense account...			11.	12.
13-14.	Close the supplies expense account.....			13.	14.
15-16.	Close the income summary account (net income balance)...................			15.	16.
17-18.	Close the income summary account (net loss balance)......................			17.	18.
19-20.	Close the owner's drawing account.....			19.	20.

Unit B—Analyzing Adjusting Entries and Closing Entries

DIRECTIONS: After each statement given below, place a check mark (√) in one of the Answers columns to indicate your answer.

	Answers		For
	True	False	Scoring
0. Transfers of amounts from one ledger account to another should be made only as a result of posting journal entries..	√		0. √
21. The income statement columns of the work sheet contain the data for journalizing the adjusting entries..			21.
22. After all adjusting entries are posted, the amount of the beginning merchandise inventory appears on the credit side of the income summary account..........			22.
23. The posting of the adjusting entry for beginning merchandise inventory cancels the debit amount in the merchandise inventory account.......................			23.
24. After all adjusting entries are posted, the amount of the ending merchandise inventory appears on the credit side of the merchandise inventory account........			24.
25. The ending merchandise inventory is a deduction from the cost of merchandise available for sale...			25.
26. The balance of the income summary account is closed into the owner's drawing account...			26.
27. One reason for recording closing entries is to bring the owner's capital account in the general ledger up to date...			27.
28. The balances of all revenue accounts are transferred to the debit side of the income summary account..			28.
29. A closing entry is made to close the drawing account into the income summary account...			29.
30. After all closing entries are posted, the balance of the owner's capital account is the owner's new capital at the end of the fiscal period......................			30.
31. After all closing entries are posted, the income statement accounts are the only general ledger accounts that have balances.................................			31.
32. When a four-column general ledger account is closed, a line should be drawn across both the Debit and Credit Balance columns...........................			32.
33. The purpose of the post-closing trial balance is to prove the equality of debits and credits in the general ledger..			33.

Chapter 17 ■ **185**

DIRECTIONS: For each of the following items, select the answer that best completes the sentence. Then print in the Answers column at the right the capital letter identifying your choice.

	Answers	For Scoring

0. After the adjusting entry for supplies has been posted, the balance of the supplies account represents the value of supplies
   (A) inventory at the beginning of the fiscal period   **(B)** bought during the fiscal period
   (C) used during the fiscal period   **(D)** inventory at the end of the fiscal period........ *D* 0. ✓

34. After the adjusting entry for supplies has been posted, the balance of the supplies expense account represents the value of supplies
    (A) inventory at the beginning of the fiscal period   **(B)** bought during the fiscal period
    (C) used during the fiscal period   **(D)** inventory at the end of the fiscal period........ 34.

35. After the adjusting entry for prepaid insurance has been posted, the balance of the prepaid insurance account represents the value of insurance premiums
    (A) prepaid at the beginning of the fiscal period   **(B)** prepaid during the fiscal period
    (C) expired during the fiscal period   **(D)** prepaid at the end of the fiscal period....... 35.

36. After the adjusting entry for prepaid insurance has been posted, the balance of the insurance expense account represents the value of insurance premiums.........................
    (A) prepaid at the beginning of the fiscal period   **(B)** prepaid during the fiscal period
    (C) expired during the fiscal period   **(D)** prepaid at the end of the fiscal period....... 36.

37. The adjusting entry for the beginning merchandise inventory includes a credit to
    (A) Income Summary   **(B)** Merchandise Inventory   **(C)** Purchases   **(D)** Sales... 37.

38. After the adjusting entry for beginning merchandise inventory has been posted, the merchandise inventory account has a
    (A) debit balance   **(B)** credit balance   **(C)** zero balance.....).................... 38.

39. After the adjusting entry for beginning merchandise inventory has been posted, the income summary account has a
    (A) debit balance   **(B)** credit balance   **(C)** zero balance......................... 39.

40. After the adjusting entry for ending merchandise inventory has been posted, the merchandise inventory account has a
    (A) debit balance   **(B)** credit balance   **(C)** zero balance......................... 40.

41. The work sheet columns used primarily by an accountant as the source for the journal entries needed to close ledger accounts at the end of the fiscal period are the
    (A) Trial Balance columns   **(B)** Adjustments columns   **(C)** Income Statement columns
    (D) Balance Sheet columns... 41.

42. After the journal entry to close the cost and the expense accounts has been posted, the purchases account has a
    (A) debit balance   **(B)** credit balance   **(C)** zero balance......................... 42.

43. After the journal entry to close the cost and the expense accounts has been posted, each expense account has a
    (A) debit balance   **(B)** credit balance   **(C)** zero balance......................... 43.

44. After the journal entry to close the revenue account has been posted, the sales account has a
    (A) debit balance   **(B)** credit balance   **(C)** zero balance......................... 44.

45. After the journal entry to close the income summary account has been posted, the income summary account has a
    (A) debit balance   **(B)** credit balance   **(C)** zero balance......................... 45.

46. After the journal entry to close the owner's drawing account has been posted, the drawing account has a
    (A) debit balance   **(B)** credit balance   **(C)** zero balance......................... 46.

47. After all closing entries have been posted, the accounts that remain open are the
    (A) asset, liability, and owner's capital account   **(B)** owner's capital, revenue, and cost accounts   **(C)** revenue, cost, and expense accounts............................... 47.

48. In taking a post-closing trial balance, the accountant lists
    (A) the accounts in alphabetic order
    (B) only those accounts that have balances
    (C) all the general ledger accounts.. 48.

Drill 17-D 1 is on page 188.

Business 3

Business 2

[1, 2]

Adjusting entries
Business 1

Adjusting entries

DRILL 17-D 1, p. 300
[1, 2]

Closing entries

DRILL 17-D 3, p. 301
[1, 2]

[1-7]

			ACCT. NO.	TRIAL BALANCE		ADJUSTMENTS		INCOME STATEMENT		BALANCE SHEET	
				1	2	3	4	5	6	7	8
ACCOUNT TITLE				DEBIT	CREDIT	DEBIT	CREDIT	DEBIT	CREDIT	DEBIT	CREDIT

ACCOUNT TITLE	ACCT. NO.	TRIAL BALANCE		ADJUSTMENTS		INCOME STATEMENT		BALANCE SHEET	
		1	2	3	4	5	6	7	8
		DEBIT	CREDIT	DEBIT	CREDIT	DEBIT	CREDIT	DEBIT	CREDIT
1									
2									
3									
4									
5									
6									
7									
8									
9									
10									
11									
12									
13									
14									
15									
16									
17									
18									
19									
20									
21									
22									
23									
24									
25									

GENERAL LEDGER

ACCOUNT *Cash*   ACCOUNT NO. *11*

DATE	ITEM	POST. REF.	DEBIT	CREDIT	BALANCE DEBIT	BALANCE CREDIT
19-- Apr. 1	Balance	✓			197730	
30		1	986240		1183970	
30		1		621470	562500	

ACCOUNT *Accounts Receivable*   ACCOUNT NO. *12*

DATE	ITEM	POST. REF.	DEBIT	CREDIT	BALANCE DEBIT	BALANCE CREDIT
19-- Apr. 1	Balance	✓			251350	
30		1	1144800		1396150	
30		1		837310	558840	

ACCOUNT *Merchandise Inventory*   ACCOUNT NO. *13*

DATE	ITEM	POST. REF.	DEBIT	CREDIT	BALANCE DEBIT	BALANCE CREDIT
19-- Apr. 1	Balance	✓			1702490	

ACCOUNT *Supplies*   ACCOUNT NO. *14*

DATE	ITEM	POST. REF.	DEBIT	CREDIT	BALANCE DEBIT	BALANCE CREDIT
19-- Apr. 1	Balance	✓			18155	
18		1	37525		55680	

ACCOUNT *Prepaid Insurance*   ACCOUNT NO. *15*

DATE	ITEM	POST. REF.	DEBIT	CREDIT	BALANCE DEBIT	BALANCE CREDIT
19-- Apr. 1	Balance	✓			47400	

ACCOUNT *Accounts Payable* ACCOUNT NO. 21

DATE	ITEM	POST. REF.	DEBIT	CREDIT	BALANCE DEBIT	BALANCE CREDIT
19-- Apr. 1	Balance	✓				105212
14		1		21481		126693
30		1		498212		624905
30		1	454722			170183

ACCOUNT *Marc Du Bois, Capital* ACCOUNT NO. 31

DATE	ITEM	POST. REF.	DEBIT	CREDIT	BALANCE DEBIT	BALANCE CREDIT
19-- Apr. 1	Balance	✓				2111913

ACCOUNT *Marc Du Bois, Drawing* ACCOUNT NO. 32

DATE	ITEM	POST. REF.	DEBIT	CREDIT	BALANCE DEBIT	BALANCE CREDIT
19-- Apr. 15		1	33000		33000	

ACCOUNT *Income Summary* ACCOUNT NO. 33

DATE	ITEM	POST. REF.	DEBIT	CREDIT	BALANCE DEBIT	BALANCE CREDIT

ACCOUNT *Sales* ACCOUNT NO. 41

DATE	ITEM	POST. REF.	DEBIT	CREDIT	BALANCE DEBIT	BALANCE CREDIT
19-- Apr. 30		1		1293730		1293730

ACCOUNT *Purchases* ACCOUNT NO. 51

DATE	ITEM	POST. REF.	DEBIT	CREDIT	BALANCE DEBIT	BALANCE CREDIT
19-- Apr. 30		1	482168		482168	

ACCOUNT *Delivery Expense*　　　　　　　　ACCOUNT NO. 61

DATE	ITEM	POST. REF.	DEBIT	CREDIT	BALANCE DEBIT	BALANCE CREDIT
19-- Apr. 16		1	11648		11648	
30		1	18316		29964	

ACCOUNT *Insurance Expense*　　　　　　　　ACCOUNT NO. 62

DATE	ITEM	POST. REF.	DEBIT	CREDIT	BALANCE DEBIT	BALANCE CREDIT

ACCOUNT *Miscellaneous Expense*　　　　　　　ACCOUNT NO. 63

DATE	ITEM	POST. REF.	DEBIT	CREDIT	BALANCE DEBIT	BALANCE CREDIT
19-- Apr. 4		1	3284		3284	

ACCOUNT *Rent Expense*　　　　　　　　　ACCOUNT NO. 64

DATE	ITEM	POST. REF.	DEBIT	CREDIT	BALANCE DEBIT	BALANCE CREDIT
19-- Apr. 1		1	44500		44500	

ACCOUNT *Salary Expense*　　　　　　　　ACCOUNT NO. 65

DATE	ITEM	POST. REF.	DEBIT	CREDIT	BALANCE DEBIT	BALANCE CREDIT
19-- Apr. 15		1	28000		28000	
30		1	28000		56000	

ACCOUNT *Supplies Expense*　　　　　　　　ACCOUNT NO. 66

DATE	ITEM	POST. REF.	DEBIT	CREDIT	BALANCE DEBIT	BALANCE CREDIT

[3]

[4]

[9]

ACCOUNT TITLE	ACCT. NO.	DEBIT	CREDIT

Work at the end of the fiscal period

COMBINATION JOURNAL

PAGE

| | CASH | | DATE | ACCOUNT TITLE | Doc. No. | Post. Ref. | GENERAL | |
	DEBIT	CREDIT					DEBIT	CREDIT
1								
2								
3								
4								
5								
6								
7								
8								
9								
10								
11								
12								
13								
14								
15								
16								
17								
18								
19								
20								
21								
22								
23								
24								
25								
26								
27								
28								
29								
30								
31								
32								

Perfect Score..35

Deduct.......—

Your Score...—

Name _____

Date _____ Class _____

Checked by _____

Unit A—Business Vocabulary

DIRECTIONS: Select the term in Column I that best completes the statement in Column II. Then print the identifying letter of that term in the Answers column.

	Column I	Column II	Answers	For Scoring
A	— automation	0. The recording, classifying, sorting, calculating, summarizing, and reporting of data is called...............	I	0. √
B	— automated data processing system	1. The procedures, forms, and machines used to provide data when needed are called a..........................		1.
C	— central processing unit	2. Working with data according to precise procedures is called..		2.
D	— chart of accounts setup form	3. Data that are received for processing and put into a system are called.....................................		3.
E	— computer	4. Filing or holding data until they are needed is called....		4.
F	— computer program	5. The information produced by a data processing system is		
G	— computer service center	called..		5.
H	— data	6. The process by which work is done mostly by machines with a minimum amount of human effort is called......		6.
I	— data processing	7. A system using automated machines to process data is		
J	— data processing system	called an.....................................		7.
K	— electronic data processing system	8. A group of interconnected machines capable of processing data according to stored instructions is called a.........		8.
L	— input	9. A system using a computer to process data is called an...		9.
M	— ledger setup form	10. The unit of a computer system that performs the processing instructions and controls the other machines is called the.		10.
N	— manual data processing system	11. A set of instructions followed by a computer to process data is called a..................................		11.
O	— output			
P	— processing	12. A person who prepares a computer program is called a..................		12.
Q	— programmer	13. A business established for the purpose of providing computer services for a fee is called a		13.
R	— storage	14. A form used in an ADP system to describe the data from the chart of accounts and the arrangement of these data on the reports is called a.................................		14.

Unit B—Basic Principles of Data Processing

DIRECTIONS: After each statement given below, place a check mark (√) in one of the Answers columns to indicate your answer.

	Answers		For Scoring
	True	False	
0. A data processing system includes the handling of all the facts of a business..........	√		0. √
15. The basic principles in planning for an automated data processing system are different from those followed in planning for a manual data processing system................			15.
16. Accuracy is more important in a manual data processing system than in an automated data processing system....................................			16.
17. A total data processing system consists of three phases — input, processing, and output.			17.
18. The electronic data processing system is the most common type of automated data processing system....................................			18.
19. The basic accounting principles change when an automated system is used.........			19.
20. Machines are designed to work more efficiently with alphabetic names than with account numbers....................................			20.
21. Businesses that use ADP will use at least a five-digit account number in their chart of accounts....................................			21.
22. In an automated accounting system, accounts in both the general ledger and the subsidiary ledgers must be assigned account numbers....................			22.

Unit C—Examining the Chart of Accounts Setup Form

DIRECTIONS: In the chart of accounts setup ruling illustrated below, the position of each part of the entry for the balance sheet is labeled with a capital letter. Locate where each of the items is written by printing the proper identifying letter in the Answers column.

CHART OF ACCOUNTS SETUP

NAME OF BUSINESS _____A_____   CLIENT NUMBER __330__

	ACCT. No.	DATA TYPE	DESCRIPTION
1	B	C	D
2		E	
3			
4			
5			F
6		G	
7			
8			
9			H
10		I	
11			
12			

	Answers	For Scoring
0. Name of business	A	0. ✓
23. Division name *Liabilities*		23.
24. Number assigned to each account		24.
25. Title of each asset account		25.
26. Type of data that appears on each line		26.
27. Division name *Assets*		27.
28. Title of each liability account		28.
29. Division name *Capital*		29.
30. Title of capital account		30.

Unit D—Assigning Account Numbers to New Accounts

DIRECTIONS: Below in Column II, for each of the new accounts given in their proper sequence with existing accounts, select the three-digit number in Column I required to complete the new account number. Then print the identifying letter of the number in the Answers column.

Column I

A — 001
B — 100
C — 125
D — 200
E — 250
F — 300
G — 375
H — 500
I — 501
J — 510
K — 520
L — 650
M — 675
N — 750
O — 751
P — 875

Column II	Answers	For Scoring
13000 Merchandise Inventory		
0. 13 ? STORE SUPPLIES	H	0. ✓
14000 Office Supplies		
31. 14 ? PREPAID INSURANCE		31.
14500 Store Equipment		
61000 Advertising Expense		
32. 61 ? DELIVERY EXPENSE		32.
33. 61 ? INSURANCE EXPENSE		33.
61500 Miscellaneous Expense		
34. 61 ? SALARY EXPENSE		34.
35. 61 ? STORE SUPPLIES EXPENSE		35.
62000 Utilities Expense		

Adding new accounts to the general ledger

Account Number	Account Title
13000	Merchandise Inventory
_____	Store Supplies
14000	Office Supplies
15000	Prepaid Insurance
_____	Store Equipment
15250	Office Equipment
61000	Advertising Expense
_____	Delivery Expense
61500	Insurance Expense
_____	Office Supplies Expense
63000	Salary Expense
_____	Store Supplies Expense
64000	Utilities Expense

DRILL 18-D 2, p. 324

Adding new accounts to the subsidiary ledger

Customer Number	Customer Name
10020	Joyce Abler
_____	George Adams
10030	Leonard Adams
10040	John Adkins
_____	Charles Alexander
_____	Mary Allison
10050	Loren Anderson
10060	Rodney Anthony
_____	Susan Arnold
10065	Kay Arthur
10070	Nancy Atkins
_____	Warren Atkins
10080	LeRoy Austin

CHART OF ACCOUNTS SETUP

NAME OF BUSINESS _____

CLIENT NUMBER _____ 382

	Acct. No.	Data Type	DESCRIPTION
1			
2			
3			
4			
5			
6			
7			
8			
9			
10			
11			
12			
13			
14			
15			
16			
17			
18			
19			
20			
21			
22			
23			
24			
25			
26			
27			
28			
29			
30			
31			
32			
33			
34			

DATA TYPE

PREPARED BY

1 = DIVISION NAME

3 = NAME
SUBSIDIARY LEDGER

2 = ACCOUNT TITLE
GENERAL LEDGER

Chart of accounts setup form for a subsidiary ledger

CHART OF ACCOUNTS SETUP

NAME OF BUSINESS _____

CLIENT NUMBER _____ *382*

	ACCT. No.	DATA TYPE	DESCRIPTION
1			
2			
3			
4			
5			
6			
7			
8			
9			
10			
11			
12			
13			
14			
15			
16			
17			
18			
19			
20			
21			
22			
23			
24			
25			
26			
27			
28			
29			
30			
31			
32			
33			
34			

DATA TYPE

1 = DIVISION NAME

2 = ACCOUNT TITLE
GENERAL LEDGER

3 = NAME
SUBSIDIARY LEDGER

PREPARED BY

CHART OF ACCOUNTS SETUP

NAME OF BUSINESS _____

CLIENT NUMBER _____

	Acct. No.	Data Type	Description
1			
2			
3			
4			
5			
6			
7			
8			
9			
10			
11			
12			
13			
14			
15			
16			
17			
18			
19			
20			
21			
22			
23			
24			
25			
26			
27			
28			
29			
30			
31			
32			
33			
34			

DATA TYPE

1 = DIVISION NAME

2 = ACCOUNT TITLE
GENERAL LEDGER

3 = NAME
SUBSIDIARY LEDGER

PREPARED BY

[1]

Adding new accounts to the general ledger
chart of accounts

Account Number	Account
_____	Store Supplies
_____	Office Supplies
_____	Store Equipment
_____	Office Equipment
_____	Office Supplies Expense
_____	Store Supplies Expense

[2]

CHART OF ACCOUNTS SETUP

NAME OF BUSINESS _____ CLIENT NUMBER _____ *423*

	ACCT. No.	DATA TYPE	DESCRIPTION
1			
2			
3			
4			
5			
6			
7			
8			
9			
10			
11			
12			
13			
14			
15			

DATA TYPE

1 = DIVISION NAME   3 = NAME
                                    SUBSIDIARY LEDGER

2 = ACCOUNT TITLE
     GENERAL LEDGER

PREPARED BY

[1]

Customer Number	Customer Name	Customer Number	Customer Name
_____	Allen Abbey	_____	James Gorthy
_____	Gary Anderson	_____	Louis Gray
_____	Floyd Baker	_____	John Martin
_____	Donald Barr	_____	George Mason
_____	Susan Goodrich	_____	Carl Woods

[2]

CHART OF ACCOUNTS SETUP

NAME OF BUSINESS _____ CLIENT NUMBER _____ *423*

	ACCT. No.	DATA TYPE	DESCRIPTION
1			
2			
3			
4			
5			
6			
7			
8			
9			
10			
11			
12			
13			
14			
15			

DATA TYPE	PREPARED BY
1 = DIVISION NAME 3 = NAME SUBSIDIARY LEDGER 2 = ACCOUNT TITLE GENERAL LEDGER	

Perfect Score..50

Deduct.......—

Your Score...—

Name

Date

Class

Checked by

Unit A—Identifying Flowchart Symbols

DIRECTIONS: Match each item in Column II with its flowchart symbol shown in Column I. Then print the identifying letter of that symbol in the Answers column.

Column I

 A —

 E —

 I —

 B —

 F —

 J —

 C —

G —

K —

D —

H —

Column II	Answers	For Scoring
0. Punched card.....	*D*	0. √
1. Keying operation..		1.
2. File.............		2.
3. Input/output.....		3.
4. Processing........		4.
5. Automatic flow lines.............		5.
6. Document........		6.
7. Magnetic disk.....		7.
8. Manual flow lines..		8.
9. Manual operation.		9.
10. Data............		10.

Unit B—Business Vocabulary

DIRECTIONS: Complete each item in Column II by selecting one of the terms given in Column I. Then print the identifying letter of that term in the Answers column.

Column I

A — automated data processing cycle
B — control total
C — data location
D — data processing cycle
E — entry register
F — fields
G — input media
H — journal entry transmittal
I — ledger transmittal
J — printout
K — punched card
L — system flowchart
M — verifying

Column II	Answers	For Scoring
0. A complete set of procedures followed in a data processing system is called a..................................	*D*	0. √
11. The complete set of procedures followed when automated equipment is used in a data processing system is called an..		11.
12. The form of the data prepared for processing by automated equipment is called..............................		12.
13. A card in which holes have been punched to represent data is called a...................................		13.
14. Checking the accuracy of data in any form is called.......		14.
15. The output of the computer in human-readable form is called the...................................		15.
16. The punched card columns reserved for the recording of specific information, such as the account number, are called....................................		16.
17. A chart that uses symbols to show the sequence of steps necessary to complete all or part of a data processing system is called a..................................		17.
18. A special form used for the recording of accounting transactions for an automated data processing system is called a...................................		18.
19. A sum of numbers used to check the accuracy of punched cards is called a..............		19.
20. A computer printout of the transaction data that are entered into a computer system is called an....................		20.

Unit C—Examining an Automated Accounting System

DIRECTIONS: After each statement given below, place a check mark (√) in one of the Answers columns to indicate your answer.

	Answers		For
	True	False	Scoring
0. The flow of data through a data processing system follows a set of procedures....	√		0. √
21. In an automated data processing cycle, a great deal of human effort is required to cause the data to move through the system................................			21.
22. The phases of the automated data processing cycle follow the same basic accounting principles as the manual data processing cycle.............................			22.
23. The same types of source documents used as a basis for journal entries in a manual data processing system are the starting points for data entries in a computerized data processing system..			23.
24. The data on the chart of accounts setup form can be read directly into the computer.			24.
25. Punched cards are the least popular form of input medium used in today's computer systems..			25.
26. The 96-column punched card is one third the size of the standard 80-column card but holds 20 percent more information....................................			26.
27. A machine that is used to determine if the data are accurately punched into cards is known as a verifier..			27.
28. Some computers have an input device that is capable of reading data recorded only on punched cards..			28.
29. While all of the units in an electronic data processing system combine to form a computer, the central processing unit is often referred to as "the computer"......			29.
30. The arithmetic/logic unit is a part of the input unit of the computer............			30.
31. The internal storage capacity of most computers is not large enough to hold at one time all of the data to be processed in a typical job..........................			31.
32. The internal storage of a computer is sometimes referred to as its "memory.".....			32.
33. The control unit within the central processing unit tells each of the other parts of a computer what to do, when to do it, and how to do it.........................			33.
34. Storage units attached to and under the control of the central processing unit are known as auxiliary storage..			34.
35. Data may be transferred from auxiliary storage to the arithmetic/logic unit only during the input phase...			35.
36. Each of the disks in a disk pack look something like a phonograph record........			36.
37. The magnetic disk drive is linked to and controlled by the input unit............			37.
38. Some computer systems use magnetic tape as internal storage..................			38.
39. The printer is the most common output device of computers handling accounting data...			39.
40. The console typewriter is a major output device in most computer systems.......			40.
41. The cathode-ray tube has become a common output device in some computer systems..			41.
42. Using the general ledger chart of accounts setup form, the computer center punches one card for each division of the ledger....................................			42.
43. The fields in a punched card can not vary in length..........................			43.
44. The magnetic disk is used to store the ledger data in an automated accounting system...			44.
45. One computer program is needed for the complete automated accounting cycle.....			45.
46. Punched cards are the most common type of auxiliary storage media for computer programs..			46.
47. In an automated data processing system, the punched cards containing the data for the opening entry represent the journal of a manual data processing system...			47.
48. A journal entry transmittal is also known as a transaction transmittal..........			48.
49. The special control totals on the journal entry transmittal form are used to check the accuracy of the punched cards that are prepared from the data recorded on the journal entry transmittal...			49.
50. One disadvantage of using a journal entry transmittal is all source documents are kept in the accounting department...			50.

Analyzing punched cards

1. _____

2. _____

3. _____

4. _____

5. _____

6. _____

7. _____

8. _____

DRILL 19-D 2, p. 350

Reading punched cards

1. _____

2. _____

JOURNAL ENTRY TRANSMITTAL

CLIENT NUMBER _____   DATE _____/_____/_____   PAGE_____ OF _____ PAGES

	ACCT. No.	CHECK No.	PURCH. No.	SALES No.	RCPT. No.	COMMENTS	DEBIT	CREDIT	
1									1
2									2
3									3
4									4
5									5
6									6
7									7
8									8
9									9
10									10
11									11
12									12
13									13
14									14
15									15
16									16
17									17
18									18
19									19
20									20
21									21
22									22
23									23
24									24
25									25

SUM OF DEBIT ENTRIES		PREPARED BY
SUM OF CREDIT ENTRIES		
SUM OF ACCOUNT NUMBERS		

Recording the opening entry for
a general ledger

					JOURNAL ENTRY TRANSMITTAL			
	CLIENT NUMBER _____			DATE __/__/__		PAGE_____ OF _____ PAGES		

	ACCT. No.	CHECK No.	PURCH. No.	SALES No.	RCPT. No.	COMMENTS	DEBIT	CREDIT	
1									1
2									2
3									3
4									4
5									5
6									6
7									7
8									8
9									9
10									10
11									11
12									12
13									13
14									14
15									15
16									16
17									17
18									18
19									19
20									20
21									21
22									22
23									23
24									24
25									25

SUM OF DEBIT ENTRIES		PREPARED BY
SUM OF CREDIT ENTRIES		
SUM OF ACCOUNT NUMBERS		

JOURNAL ENTRY TRANSMITTAL

CLIENT NUMBER _____   DATE ____/____/____   PAGE _____ OF _____ PAGES

	Acct. No.	Check No.	Purch. No.	Sales No.	Rcpt. No.	COMMENTS	DEBIT	CREDIT	
1									1
2									2
3									3
4									4
5									5
6									6
7									7
8									8
9									9
10									10
11									11
12									12
13									13
14									14
15									15
16									16
17									17
18									18
19									19
20									20
21									21
22									22
23									23
24									24
25									25

SUM OF DEBIT ENTRIES

SUM OF CREDIT ENTRIES

SUM OF ACCOUNT NUMBERS

PREPARED BY

Perfect Score..38

Deduct.......—

Your Score...—

Name _____

Date _____ Class _____

Checked by _____

Unit A—Analyzing the System Flowchart for the Processing of Daily Transactions

DIRECTIONS: Read pages 359–360 in Chapter 20. Then match each item in Column II below with its flowchart symbol in Column I. Print the identifying letter of that symbol in the Answers column.

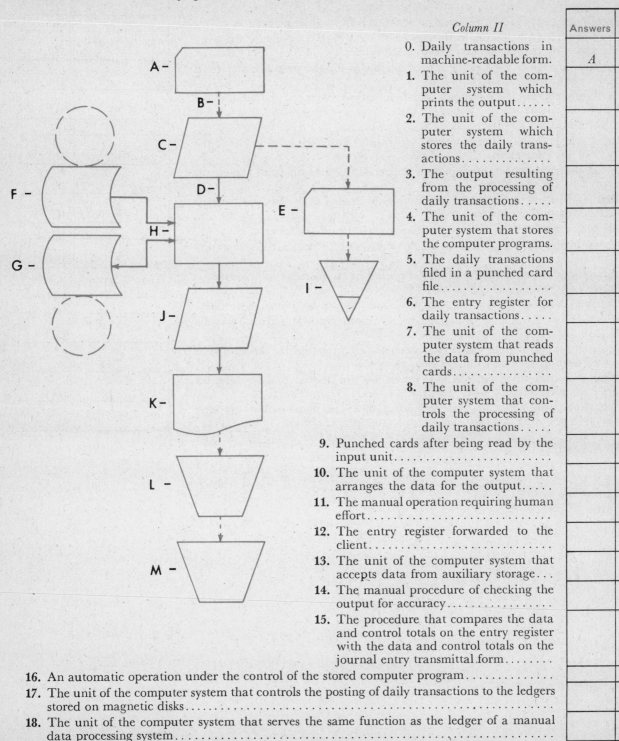

Column II	Answers	For Scoring
0. Daily transactions in machine-readable form.	*A*	0. ✓
1. The unit of the computer system which prints the output......		1.
2. The unit of the computer system which stores the daily transactions..............		2.
3. The output resulting from the processing of daily transactions.....		3.
4. The unit of the computer system that stores the computer programs.		4.
5. The daily transactions filed in a punched card file..................		5.
6. The entry register for daily transactions.....		6.
7. The unit of the computer system that reads the data from punched cards...............		7.
8. The unit of the computer system that controls the processing of daily transactions.....		8.
9. Punched cards after being read by the input unit........................		9.
10. The unit of the computer system that arranges the data for the output.....		10.
11. The manual operation requiring human effort............................		11.
12. The entry register forwarded to the client.........................		12.
13. The unit of the computer system that accepts data from auxiliary storage...		13.
14. The manual procedure of checking the output for accuracy..............		14.
15. The procedure that compares the data and control totals on the entry register with the data and control totals on the journal entry transmittal form........		15.
16. An automatic operation under the control of the stored computer program..............		16.
17. The unit of the computer system that controls the posting of daily transactions to the ledgers stored on magnetic disks........................		17.
18. The unit of the computer system that serves the same function as the ledger of a manual data processing system.......................		18.

DIRECTIONS: After each statement given below, place a check mark (√) in one of the Answers columns to indicate your answer.

Statement	Answers True	Answers False	For Scoring
0. The methods of journalizing daily transactions for an automated data processing system are the same regardless of the nature of the business...............		√	0. √
19. The arranging of transactions by similar groups is known as batching..........			19.
20. The batching procedure increases the number of journal entries..............			20.
21. With the batching procedure, the total of the group of transactions is entered as one combined entry..			21.
22. A machine that is used to record in handwritten form the information about a business transaction is known as an autographic register..................			22.
23. The source document for cash received on account is the cash register tape.......			23.
24. At the end of each day, the total cash sales for the day shown on the cash register tape is recorded on the journal entry transmittal form..................			24.
25. The purchase invoice is used as the source document for the journal entry for a purchase of merchandise on account................................			25.
26. At the end of each day, all purchases of merchandise on account for the day are recorded on the journal entry transmittal form........................			26.
27. A sales invoice is used for all cash sales.................................			27.
28. The control totals and the journal entry transmittal form are used to check the equality of debits and credits...................................			28.
29. At the end of each monthly fiscal period, the schedules and financial statements are prepared by the computer...................................			29.
30. The subsidiary ledgers in automated accounting are located in the auxiliary storage media connected to the input unit of the computer system...............			30.
31. Magnetic disks may be used to store the data for the subsidiary ledgers.........			31.
32. The general ledger data are stored on magnetic disks in an automated accounting system...			32.
33. All computations are done by the computer according to instructions provided by the computer operator....................................			33.
34. A computer printout of the trial balance is needed to plan the adjusting entries..			34.
35. The computer has the ability of making the decisions needed to plan adjusting entries..			35.
36. In automated accounting the financial statements are prepared by the computer system after the adjusting entries have been processed..................			36.
37. The computer printouts of the financial statements are needed to determine the necessary closing entries....................................			37.
38. In automated accounting the post-closing trial balance is prepared by the computer system from data on the magnetic disks used for the general ledger.............			38.

Analyzing the completed journal entry transmittal

1. _____

2. _____

3. _____

4. _____

_____

_____

5. _____

_____

_____

6. _____

7. _____

8. _____

Analyzing a systems flowchart

DRILL 20-D 2, p. 373

1. _____

2. _____

_____

_____

3. _____

4. _____

5. _____

6. _____

_____

_____

_____

JOURNAL ENTRY TRANSMITTAL

CLIENT NUMBER _____   DATE ____/____/____   PAGE_____ OF _____PAGES

	ACCT. No.	CHECK No.	PURCH. No.	SALES No.	RCPT. No.	COMMENTS	DEBIT	CREDIT	
1									1
2									2
3									3
4									4
5									5
6									6
7									7
8									8
9									9
10									10
11									11
12									12
13									13
14									14
15									15
16									16
17									17
18									18
19									19
20									20
21									21
22									22
23									23
24									24
25									25

SUM OF DEBIT ENTRIES

SUM OF CREDIT ENTRIES

PREPARED BY

SUM OF ACCOUNT NUMBERS

Recording adjusting entries using a journal entry transmittal

JOURNAL ENTRY TRANSMITTAL

CLIENT NUMBER _____   DATE ___/___/___   PAGE____ OF ____ PAGES

	Acct. No.	Check No.	Purch. No.	Sales No.	Rcpt. No.	COMMENTS	DEBIT	CREDIT	
1									1
2									2
3									3
4									4
5									5
6									6
7									7
8									8
9									9
10									10
11									11
12									12
13									13
14									14
15									15
16									16
17									17
18									18
19									19
20									20
21									21
22									22
23									23
24									24
25									25

SUM OF DEBIT ENTRIES

SUM OF CREDIT ENTRIES

SUM OF ACCOUNT NUMBERS

PREPARED BY

JOURNAL ENTRY TRANSMITTAL

CLIENT NUMBER _____   DATE _____ / _____ / _____   PAGE_____ OF _____PAGES

	Acct. No.	Check No.	Purch. No.	Sales No.	Rcpt. No.	COMMENTS	DEBIT	CREDIT	
1									1
2									2
3									3
4									4
5									5
6									6
7									7
8									8
9									9
10									10
11									11
12									12
13									13
14									14
15									15
16									16
17									17
18									18
19									19
20									20
21									21
22									22
23									23
24									24
25									25
26									26

SUM OF DEBIT ENTRIES

SUM OF CREDIT ENTRIES

SUM OF ACCOUNT NUMBERS

PREPARED BY

Journalizing transactions using a journal entry transmittal

JOURNAL ENTRY TRANSMITTAL

CLIENT NUMBER _____   DATE ___/___/___   PAGE_____ OF _____ PAGES

	Acct. No.	Check No.	Purch. No.	Sales No.	Rcpt. No.	COMMENTS	DEBIT	CREDIT	
1									1
2									2
3									3
4									4
5									5
6									6
7									7
8									8
9									9
10									10
11									11
12									12
13									13
14									14
15									15
16									16
17									17
18									18
19									19
20									20
21									21
22									22
23									23
24									24
25									25

SUM OF DEBIT ENTRIES		PREPARED BY
SUM OF CREDIT ENTRIES		
SUM OF ACCOUNT NUMBERS		

Preparing a systems flowchart

*Use this page to prepare
your systems flowchart.*

BONUS PROBLEM 20-B, p. 375

BONUS PROBLEM 20-B, p. 375

Perfect Score..53

Deduct.......—

Your Score...—

Name_____

Date_____ Class_____

Checked by_____

Unit A—Analyzing Payroll Records

DIRECTIONS: After each statement given below, place a check mark (√) in one of the Answers columns to indicate your answer.

	Answers		For
	True	False	Scoring
0. Many large companies use automated data processing equipment to process their payrolls...	√		0. √
1. The basic principles in maintaining payroll records differ when automated methods are used.......................................			1.
2. Payroll records showing payments and deductions must be kept by a company......			2.
3. A business is required by law to withhold certain payroll taxes from the salaries it pays to its employees and to forward these taxes to the government....................			3.
4. A single person who earns $200.00 a week pays less federal income tax than a married person with the same weekly earnings..................................			4.
5. An employee receives a reduction in the amount withheld for income tax for each exemption claimed			5.
6. An employee is allowed one exemption for each person who qualifies as a dependent...			6.
7. A person must fill out and sign Form W-4, Employee's Withholding Exemption Certificate, each time federal income tax is withheld from his pay.................			7.
8. The marital status and the number of exemptions claimed by an employee are identified on his Form W-4..			8.
9. All states and cities levy income taxes that employers are required to withhold from each employee's pay..			9.
10. The FICA tax is paid by both employees and employers........................			10.
11. The employer pays a different rate of FICA tax on an employee's earnings than each employee does on personal wages..			11.
12. The federal unemployment tax is paid entirely by the employer and is used only for administrative expenses			12.
13. Banks are required to furnish the federal government with a listing of interest payments of $10.00 or more giving the names and social security numbers of the payees...			13.
14. Every employee in an occupation covered by the social security laws is required to have a social security number..			14.
15. A social security card is issued for a small charge by the Social Security Administration to anyone upon request			15.
16. If a social security card is lost, the person may apply for a new social security number			16.
17. A woman who changes her name by court order or by marriage should notify the Social Security Administration of the change..................................			17.
18. The payroll time sheet is used as the basic source of data for the preparation of the employee's earnings record			18.
19. The individual employee's earnings record is used as the source document to prepare each payroll check..			19.
20. The employer is required by law to retain payroll records on file for a minimum period of four years..			20.
21. A payroll change sheet is used when employees are paid by check.................			21.
22. When a payroll is paid in cash, a business prepares for each employee a separate payroll receipt that itemizes gross pay, deductions, and net pay..................			22.
23. A business that uses self-processed pay checks must write individual checks for each of its employees...			23.
24. In an automated accounting system, the time card used for payroll is in the form of a punched card...			24.

Unit B—Business Vocabulary

DIRECTIONS: Complete each item in Column II by selecting one of the terms given in Column I. Then print the identifying letter of that term in the Answers column.

Column I

A — employee's earnings record
B — exemption
C — federal unemployment tax
D — FICA tax
E — medicare
F — pay period
G — payroll
H — payroll register
I — payroll taxes
J — pegboard
K — ringing in and ringing out
L — social security taxes
M — state unemployment tax
N — total earnings
O — write-it-once principle
P — year-to-date earnings

Column II

		Answers	For Scoring
0.	The period covered by the wage or salary payment is called a....................................	F	0. ✓
25.	A list of employees that shows payments due them for a pay period is called a.........................		25.
26.	Taxes based on the payroll of a business are called.......		26.
27.	A deduction for each qualified person supported by a taxpayer is called an.............................		27.
28.	All the taxes imposed under the social security laws are called................................		28.
29.	The federal health insurance program, designed for people who have reached age 65, is popularly called..........		29.
30.	The social security tax paid to the federal government by both employees and employers for use in paying old-age, survivors, disability insurance benefits, and health insurance benefits (medicare) is called..................		30.
31.	The tax assessed by the federal government for paying state and federal administrative expenses for the unemployment program is called the......................		31.
32.	The tax assessed by the state for paying benefits to unemployed workers is called......................		32.
33.	The total pay due for the pay period before deductions is called..................................		33.
34.	A business form on which the entire payroll is recorded is called a......................		34.
35.	The business form showing details of all items affecting payments made to each employee is called an..............		35.
36.	A special board used to write the same information at one time on several separate kinds of forms held in place by a number of pegs is called a..........................		36.
37.	The procedure of producing more than one copy of the same data in only one writing is called the..............		37.

Unit C—Examining the Payroll Time Card

DIRECTIONS: The questions at the right are based on the payroll time card shown below. Indicate your answer by placing a check mark in one of the Answers columns.

Mr. Arthur's regular working hours are: 8:00 a.m. to 5:00 p.m. with a one-hour lunch period from 12:00 noon until 1:00 p.m.

EMPLOYEE NO. 6
NAME John C. Arthur
SOC. SEC. NO. 143-05-0832
WEEK ENDING June 24, 1977

Ⓙ

MORNING		AFTERNOON		OVERTIME		HOURS	
IN	OUT	IN	OUT	IN	OUT	REG	OT
7:56	12:00	12:55	5:02			8	
7:50	12:01	12:59	5:07			8	
7:51	12:01	12:50	5:04			8	
7:58	12:02	1:01	5:03	6:00	9:20	8	3⅓
8:00	12:05	12:58	5:06			8	

	HOURS	RATE	AMOUNT
REGULAR	40	4.00	160.00
OVERTIME	3⅓	6.00	20.00
TOTAL HOURS	43⅓	TOTAL EARNINGS	180.00

		Answers Yes	Answers No	For Scoring
0.	Does Mr. Arthur's payroll number change each week?..................................		✓	0. ✓
38.	Does Mr. Arthur's payroll number differ from his social security number?..................			38.
39.	Does the time card cover only one week?........			39.
40.	Did Mr. Arthur ring in early any morning during the week?..................................			40.
41.	Did he ring in late any morning?..............			41.
42.	Did he ring out early any morning?............			42.
43.	Did he ring in early any afternoon?............			43.
44.	Did Mr. Arthur receive any overtime pay for ringing in early?..........................			44.
45.	Was he tardy any morning?...................			45.
46.	Did he ring in late any afternoon?.............			46.
47.	Did he ring out early any afternoon?...........			47.
48.	Were any deductions made from Mr. Arthur's pay for tardiness?........................			48.
49.	Did he work overtime any evening during the week?..................................			49.
50.	Is the total number of overtime hours worked by Mr. Arthur recorded on the card?.............			50.
51.	Does the hourly rate for regular hours appear on the time card?..........................			51.
52.	Does the amount of Mr. Arthurs' total earnings during the week appear on the time card?.......			52.
53.	Is the time card discarded immediately after the payroll for the week has been recorded?........			53.

Determining payroll income tax withholdings

1._____ 4._____

2._____ 5._____

3._____

Figuring total weekly earnings for employees

| Employee Number | Hours worked | | Pay Rate | Amount of pay | | Total Earnings |
	Regular	Overtime		Regular	Overtime	
1	40	2	$4.00	$160.00	$12.00	$172.00
2	40	6	4.25	_____	_____	_____
3	35	0	3.50	_____	_____	_____
4	40	3	4.50	_____	_____	_____
5	40	0	4.50	_____	_____	_____

Applying for a social security account number

ID	CN		DO	270		

APPLICATION FOR A SOCIAL SECURITY NUMBER   DO NOT WRITE IN THE ABOVE SPACE

See Instructions on Back.   Print in Black or Dark Blue Ink or Use Typewriter.

1 Print FULL NAME YOU WILL USE IN WORK OR BUSINESS   (First Name)   (Middle Name or Initial – if none, draw line ___)   (Last Name)

2 Print FULL NAME GIVEN YOU AT BIRTH

6 YOUR DATE OF BIRTH   (Month)   (Day)   (Year)

3 PLACE OF BIRTH   (City)   (County if known)   (State)

7 YOUR PRESENT AGE (Age on last birthday)

4 MOTHER'S FULL NAME AT HER BIRTH (Her maiden name)

8 YOUR SEX   MALE   FEMALE

5 FATHER'S FULL NAME (Regardless of whether living or dead)

9 YOUR COLOR OR RACE   WHITE   NEGRO   OTHER

10 HAVE YOU EVER BEFORE APPLIED FOR OR HAD A SOCIAL SECURITY, RAILROAD, OR TAX ACCOUNT NUMBER?   NO   DON'T KNOW   YES   (If "YES" Print STATE in which you applied and DATE you applied and SOCIAL SECURITY NUMBER if known)

11 YOUR MAILING ADDRESS   (Number and Street, Apt. No., P.O. Box, or Rural Route)   (City)   (State)   (Zip Code)

12 TODAY'S DATE

14 NOTICE: Whoever, with intent to falsify his or someone else's true identity, willfully furnishes or causes to be furnished false information in applying for a social security number, is subject to a fine of not more than $1,000 or imprisonment for up to 1 year, or both.

13 TELEPHONE NUMBER   Sign YOUR NAME HERE (Do Not Print)

TREASURY DEPARTMENT Internal Revenue Service   □ RESCREEN   □ ASSIGN   □ DUP ISSUED   Return completed application to nearest SOCIAL SECURITY ADMINISTRATION OFFICE

FORM SS-5 (2-73)

Employee No. 22 — Mary Glenn

SOC. SEC. NO. 283-54-3008
WEEK ENDING April 18, 19--

	MORNING IN	OUT	AFTERNOON IN	OUT	OVERTIME IN	OUT	HOURS REG	OT
M	7:59	12:00	12:58	5:00				
TU	7:58	12:01	12:57	5:01				
W	7:57	12:03	12:55	5:02				
TH	8:03	12:00	12:51	5:05				
F	7:55	12:02	1:02	5:03				

RATE 2.50
3.75

REGULAR HOURS / OVERTIME / TOTAL HOURS
AMOUNT / TOTAL EARNINGS

Employee No. 24 — Roy Hanes

SOC. SEC. NO. 295-30-4002
WEEK ENDING April 18, 19--

	MORNING IN	OUT	AFTERNOON IN	OUT	OVERTIME IN	OUT	HOURS REG	OT
M	7:58	12:03	12:58	5:02				
TU	8:04	12:01	12:55	5:01				
W	7:57	12:00	12:53	5:04	7:00	9:01		
TH	7:59	12:02	12:58	5:01				
F	7:58	12:01	1:00	5:03				

RATE 3.20
4.80

REGULAR / OVERTIME / TOTAL HOURS
AMOUNT / TOTAL EARNINGS

Employee No. 29 — Robert Klein

SOC. SEC. NO. 268-28-4140
WEEK ENDING April 18, 19--

	MORNING IN	OUT	AFTERNOON IN	OUT	OVERTIME IN	OUT	HOURS REG	OT
M	7:57	12:01	1:00	5:02	7:00	8:00		
TU	7:56	12:00	12:57	5:01				
W	7:58	12:03	12:55	5:05	6:00	8:02		
TH	7:57	12:02	12:58	5:02				
F	7:56	12:01	12:58	5:01				

RATE 3.00
4.50

REGULAR / OVERTIME / TOTAL HOURS
AMOUNT / TOTAL EARNINGS

Employee No. 21 — Herbert Lenon

SOC. SEC. NO. 278-28-4040
WEEK ENDING April 18, 19--

	MORNING IN	OUT	AFTERNOON IN	OUT	OVERTIME IN	OUT	HOURS REG	OT
M	7:56	12:00	12:58	5:01				
TU	7:57	12:01	12:52	5:08				
W	7:58	12:02	1:04	5:02				
TH	7:59	12:01	12:59	5:03				
F	8:00	12:02						

RATE 4.00
6.00

REGULAR / OVERTIME / TOTAL HOURS
AMOUNT / TOTAL EARNINGS

Employee No. 25 — Betty Murphy

SOC. SEC. NO. 285-48-3201
WEEK ENDING April 18, 19--

	MORNING IN	OUT	AFTERNOON IN	OUT	OVERTIME IN	OUT	HOURS REG	OT
M	7:57	12:02	12:55	5:02				
TU	7:56	12:02	12:59	5:03				
W	7:58	12:01	12:56	5:03	5:59	8:02		
TH	7:55	12:02	12:56	5:02				
F	7:56	12:01	12:58	5:03				

RATE 4.20
6.30

REGULAR / OVERTIME / TOTAL HOURS
AMOUNT / TOTAL EARNINGS

Employee No. 27 — Alice Watson

SOC. SEC. NO. 295-48-3201
WEEK ENDING April 18, 19--

	MORNING IN	OUT	AFTERNOON IN	OUT	OVERTIME IN	OUT	HOURS REG	OT
M	7:59	12:00	12:59	5:02	6:00	8:03		
TU	7:58	12:02	12:58	5:05				
W	7:59	12:02	12:57	5:01	5:55	8:01		
TH	7:58	12:02	12:58	5:03				
F	7:59	12:03	12:59	5:03				

RATE 3.60
5.40

REGULAR / OVERTIME / TOTAL HOURS
AMOUNT / TOTAL EARNINGS

PAYROLL REGISTER

WEEK ENDED April 18, 19——

DATE OF PAYMENT

EMPL. NO.	EMPLOYEE'S NAME	MARI-TAL STATUS	NO. OF EXEMP-TIONS	TOTAL EARNINGS	DEDUCTIONS					NET PAY	CK. NO.	
					INCOME TAX	FICA TAX	HOSP. INS.	OTHER	TOTAL			
1	22	Glenn, Mary	S	1									1
2	24	Hanes, Roy	M	3									2
3	29	Klein, Robert	S	1									3
4	21	Lenon, Herbert	M	4									4
5	25	Murphy, Betty	M	1									5
6	27	Watson, Alice	S	1									6

OTHER DEDUCTIONS: B—U.S. Savings Bonds; GI—Group Insurance; U—Union Dues; UF—United Fund

Preparing an employee's earnings record

EARNINGS RECORD FOR QUARTER ENDING

LAST NAME	FIRST	MIDDLE INITIAL

EMPLOYEE NO. _____ MARITAL STATUS _____ EXEMPTIONS _____

SOCIAL SECURITY NO. _____

POSITION _____

PAY PERIOD		TOTAL EARNINGS	DEDUCTIONS					NET PAY	ACCUMULATED EARNINGS
WEEK NO.	WEEK ENDED		INCOME TAX	FICA TAX	HOSP. INS.	OTHER	TOTAL		
1									
2									
3									
4									
5									
6									
7									
8									
9									
10									
11									
12									
13									
QUARTERLY TOTALS									

Preparing a payroll [1, 2]

PAYROLL REGISTER

DATE OF PAYMENT

WEEK ENDED

EMPL. NO.	EMPLOYEE'S NAME	MARI-TAL STATUS	NO. OF EXEMP-TIONS	TOTAL EARNINGS	DEDUCTIONS						NET PAY	CK. NO.
					INCOME TAX	FICA TAX	HOSP. INS.	OTHER	TOTAL			
1												
2												
3												
4												
5												
6												
7												
8												
9												
10												
11												
12												
13												
14												
15												
16												
17												
18												
19												
20												
21												
22												

OTHER DEDUCTIONS: B — BONDS; UF — UNITED FUND

No. 827 Date _____ 19__ $_____

GENERAL
ACCOUNT

M

No. 827

59-301
1213

To_____

_____ 19_____

For_____

Pay to the
order of _____ $_____

_____ Dollars

BAL. BRO'T. FOR'D.   8,745 50

KAHALA NATIONAL BANK
Honolulu, Hawaii   96821

MIDWAY SUPPLY COMPANY

AMT. DEPOSITED   19
DATE

TOTAL

AMT. THIS CHECK

BAL. CAR'D. FOR'D.

⑈1213⑈301⑈   267⑈0025⑈04⑈

CHECK NO. 268

PAYROLL
ACCOUNT

M

No. 268

59-301
1213

PERIOD
ENDING   19

_____ 19_____

EARNINGS $

REG. .... $_____
O.T. .... $_____

Pay to the
order of _____ $_____

DEDUCTIONS $

_____ Dollars

INC. TAX .... $_____
FICA TAX ..... $_____
GROUP INS. .. $_____
HOSP. INS. .... $_____
OTHER .... $_____

KAHALA NATIONAL BANK
Honolulu, Hawaii   96821

MIDWAY SUPPLY COMPANY

NET PAY $

⑈1213⑈301⑈   185⑈0146⑈08⑈

CHECK NO. 269

PAYROLL
ACCOUNT

M

No. 269

59-301
1213

PERIOD
ENDING   19

_____ 19_____

EARNINGS $

REG. .... $_____
O.T. .... $_____

Pay to the
order of _____ $_____

DEDUCTIONS $

_____ Dollars

INC. TAX .... $_____
FICA TAX ..... $_____
GROUP INS. .. $_____
HOSP. INS. .... $_____
OTHER .... $_____

KAHALA NATIONAL BANK
Honolulu, Hawaii   96821

MIDWAY SUPPLY COMPANY

NET PAY $

⑈1213⑈301⑈   185⑈0146⑈08⑈

Preparing a payroll

PAYROLL REGISTER

WEEK ENDED

DATE OF PAYMENT

EMPL. NO.	EMPLOYEE'S NAME	MARI-TAL STATUS	NO. OF EXEMP-TIONS	TOTAL EARNINGS	DEDUCTIONS					NET PAY	CK. NO.
					INCOME TAX	FICA TAX	HOSP. INS.	OTHER	TOTAL		
1											1
2											2
3											3
4											4
5											5
6											6
7											7
8											8
9											9
10											10
11											11
12											12
13											13
14											14
15											15
16											16
17											17
18											18
19											19
20											20
21											21
22											22

OTHER DEDUCTIONS: B — BONDS

PAYROLL REGISTER

WEEK ENDED

DATE OF PAYMENT

EMPL. NO.	EMPLOYEE'S NAME	MARITAL STATUS	NO. OF EXEMPTIONS	TOTAL EARNINGS	DEDUCTIONS				TOTAL	NET PAY	CK. NO.
					INCOME TAX	FICA TAX	HOSP. INS.	OTHER			
1											1
2											2
3											3
4											4
5											5
6											6
7											7
8											8
9											9
10											10
11											11

Use the space below for making calculations.

Perfect Score..42

Deduct.......—

Your Score...—

Name _____

Date _____ Class _____

Checked by _____

Unit A—Examining Form W-2

DIRECTIONS: The questions given below are related to Form W-2, Wage and Tax Statement. Some of the questions are based specifically on the form shown at the right; others are general in nature. Indicate your answer to each question by placing a check mark (√) in one of the Answers columns.

	Wage and Tax Statement 1977		
Johnstone Orchard 7901 Bayview Orange, TX 77630	Type or print EMPLOYER'S name, address, ZIP code and Federal identifying number.	Copy B To be filed with employee's FEDERAL tax return	
		Employer's State identifying number 31-0318521	
Employee's social security number 143-05-0832	1 Federal income tax withheld 962.00	2 Wages, tips, and other compensation 8,560.00	3 FICA employee tax withheld 513.60	4 Total FICA wages
Type or print Employee's name, address, and ZIP code below. John C. Arthur 812 Twin Hills Drive Orange, TX 77630	5 Was employee covered by a qualified pension plan, etc.? No	6	7
	8 State or local tax withheld	9 State or local wages	10 State or locality
	11 State or local tax withheld	12 State or local wages	13 State or locality

Form W-2 This information is being furnished to the Internal Revenue Service. Department of the Treasury—Internal Revenue Service

	Answers		For Scoring
	Yes	No	
0. Does the Form W-2 shown above identify the name of John C. Arthur's employer?..	√		0. √
1. Does this Form W-2 show John Arthur's net pay from Johnstone Orchard for the entire year?..			1.
2. Does this Form W-2 show how many months during 1977 Mr. Arthur was employed by Johnstone Orchard?..................................			2.
3. Does the number of John Arthur's dependents affect the amount of FICA tax withheld from his wages?.....................................			3.
4. Are the amounts withheld from the wages of all employees for income tax the same?..			4.
5. Does this Form W-2 show the total wages earned during 1977 by Mr. Arthur at Johnstone Orchard?..			5.
6. If an employee stops working for a company before the end of the calendar year, must a form W-2 report be furnished to that person within 15 days of departure?...			6.
7. In some cases are "Wages, tips and other compensation" and "Total FICA wages" shown as different amounts on an employee's Form W-2?.....................			7.
8. Is the amount withheld for Mr. Arthur's FICA tax more than the amount withheld for his federal income tax?......................................			8.
9. Does this Form W-2 show the total amount withheld from Mr. Arthur's earnings by Johnstone Orchard for his federal income tax?.........................			9.
10. Does this Form W-2 show the total amount withheld from Mr. Arthur's earnings by Johnstone Orchard for his FICA tax?..............................			10.
11. Is an employer required to provide employees with a Form W-2 report no later than January 31 of the year following the one for which the report has been completed?..			11.
12. If an employee works for several employers during the year, must that employee receive a Form W-2 report from each employer?...........................			12.
13. When John Arthur files his federal income tax return, must he attach Copy A of his Form W-2 to his return?.......................................			13.
14. Are John Arthur's total wages for 1977 from Johnstone Orchard more than his total FICA wages for 1977?......................................			14.
15. Was Johnstone Orchard required during 1977 to withhold FICA tax from John Arthur's wages every month that he worked for the company?..................			15.
16. Does this Form W-2 indicate whether John Arthur had more than one employer during 1977?...			16.
17. At the end of each year, is every employer required to send to the Internal Revenue Service one copy of each Form W-2 issued by the company?...................			17.
18. Is John Arthur permitted to keep one copy of each Form W-2 he receives?.........			18.
19. Must Johnstone Orchard provide two copies of Form W-2 to each of its employees?..			19.
20. Does this Form W-2 reveal whether John Arthur worked part time evenings during 1977 for another employer?...................................			20.

Unit B—Recording Payroll Transactions

DIRECTIONS: For each transaction given below, print in the appropriate Answers column the identifying capital letters of the accounts to be debited and credited. Select the capital letters from the account titles listed at the left.

Account Title

A — Cash

B — Employee Income Tax Payable

C — Federal Unemployment Tax Payable

D — FICA Tax Payable

E — Payroll Taxes Expense

F — Salary Expense

G — State Unemployment Tax Payable

H — U.S. Savings Bonds Payable

Transaction

		Answers		For Scoring	
		Debit	Credit	Debit	Credit
0-0.	Record employer's payroll taxes for FICA tax	E	D	0. ✓	0. ✓
21-22.	Issue check in payment of employees income tax and in payment of FICA tax			21.	22.
23-24.	Record employer's payroll taxes for federal unemployment tax			23.	24.
25-26.	Issue check in payment of U.S. Savings Bonds for employees			25.	26.
27-28.	Issue check in payment of federal unemployment tax			27.	28.
29-30.	Issue check in payment of state unemployment tax			29.	30.
31-32.	Issue check in payment of monthly payroll less deductions for income tax, FICA tax, and U.S. Savings Bonds			31.	32.
33-34.	Record employer's payroll taxes for state unemployment tax			33.	34.

Unit C—Analyzing Payroll Regulations and Records

DIRECTIONS: For each of the following items, select the answer that best completes the sentence. Then print in the Answers column at the right the capital letter identifying your choice.

	Answers	For Scoring
0. The funds with which to pay FICA benefits are raised by (A) a tax on employers only (B) a tax on employees only (C) unequal taxes on both the employer and the employee (D) equal taxes on both the employer and the employee	D	0. ✓
35. Until the amounts withheld from employees' earnings for income tax and FICA tax are sent to the Internal Revenue Service, the amounts withheld represent (A) a liability of the business (B) an expense of the business (C) an asset of the business (D) a revenue of the business		35.
36. The total of the Total Earnings column of the payroll register is debited to (A) a liability account (B) a revenue account (C) an expense account (D) an asset account		36.
37. The total of the FICA tax column of the payroll register is credited to (A) a liability account (B) an asset account (C) an expense account (D) a revenue account		37.
38. The total of the Income Tax column of the payroll register is credited to (A) a revenue account (B) an asset account (C) an expense account (D) a liability account		38.
39. The total of the Net Pay column of the payroll register is credited to (A) an expense account (B) a revenue account (C) a liability account (D) an asset account		39.
40. When the payroll is paid, the credit to Cash is equal to the (A) total deductions from earnings (B) net pay received by the employees (C) total earnings of all employees (D) total deductions for income tax and FICA tax		40.
41. When the total of the income tax and FICA tax due to the government is less than $200.00 a quarter, the employer is required to deposit the total amount in an approved bank (A) on or before the end of the month following the end of the quarter (B) only at the end of the calendar year (C) by the 15th of the following month (D) at the end of each month		41.
42. Taxes such as FICA tax, federal unemployment tax, and state unemployment tax as a group are frequently referred to as (A) city taxes (B) payroll taxes (C) income taxes (D) sales taxes		42.

Analyzing payroll transactions

PROBLEM 22-1, p. 415

Recording payrolls and payroll taxes

[1, 2]

COMBINATION JOURNAL

PAGE								GENERAL		
1	2					3	4			
CASH		DATE	ACCOUNT TITLE	Doc. No.	Post. Ref.	GENERAL				
DEBIT	CREDIT					DEBIT	CREDIT			
1										1
2										2
3										3
4										4
5										5
6										6
7										7
8										8

COMBINATION JOURNAL

PAGE 1	2						3	4	
CASH		DATE	ACCOUNT TITLE	Doc. No.	Post. Ref.	GENERAL			
DEBIT	CREDIT					DEBIT	CREDIT		

1									1
2									2
3									3
4									4
5									5
6									6
7									7
8									8
9									9
10									10
11									11
12									12
13									13
14									14
15									15
16									16
17									17
18									18
19									19
20									20
21									21
22									22
23									23
24									24
25									25
26									26
27									27
28									28
29									29
30									30
31									31
32									32
33									33
34									34

Recording and posting payroll transactions   [2, 3]

COMBINATION JOURNAL

	CASH						GENERAL	
PAGE 1	2		DATE	ACCOUNT TITLE	DOC. No.	POST. REF.	3 DEBIT	4 CREDIT
	DEBIT	CREDIT					DEBIT	CREDIT
1								
2								
3								
4								
5								
6								
7								
8								
9								
10								
11								
12								
13								
14								
15								
16								
17								
18								
19								
20								
21								
22								
23								
24								
25								
26								
27								
28								
29								
30								
31								
32								
33								
34								

Continue the combination journal on the next page.

PAGE

COMBINATION JOURNAL

CASH		DATE	ACCOUNT TITLE	DOC. No.	POST. REF.	GENERAL	
DEBIT	CREDIT					DEBIT	CREDIT

GENERAL LEDGER

ACCOUNT_____ ACCOUNT NO._____

DATE	ITEM	POST. REF.	DEBIT	CREDIT	BALANCE	
					DEBIT	CREDIT

ACCOUNT_____ ACCOUNT NO._____

DATE	ITEM	POST. REF.	DEBIT	CREDIT	BALANCE	
					DEBIT	CREDIT

ACCOUNT_____ ACCOUNT NO._____

DATE	ITEM	POST. REF.	DEBIT	CREDIT	BALANCE	
					DEBIT	CREDIT

ACCOUNT   **ACCOUNT NO.**

DATE	ITEM	POST. REF.	DEBIT	CREDIT	BALANCE	
					DEBIT	CREDIT

ACCOUNT   **ACCOUNT NO.**

DATE	ITEM	POST. REF.	DEBIT	CREDIT	BALANCE	
					DEBIT	CREDIT

ACCOUNT   **ACCOUNT NO.**

DATE	ITEM	POST. REF.	DEBIT	CREDIT	BALANCE	
					DEBIT	CREDIT

ACCOUNT   **ACCOUNT NO.**

DATE	ITEM	POST. REF.	DEBIT	CREDIT	BALANCE	
					DEBIT	CREDIT

Recording and posting payroll transactions

COMBINATION JOURNAL

	CASH							GENERAL		
	DEBIT	CREDIT	DATE	ACCOUNT TITLE	DOC. NO.	POST. REF.		DEBIT	CREDIT	
1										1
2										2
3										3
4										4
5										5
6										6
7										7
8										8
9										9
10										10
11										11
12										12
13										13
14										14
15										15
16										16
17										17
18										18
19										19
20										20
21										21
22										22
23										23
24										24
25										25
26										26
27										27
28										28
29										29
30										30
31										31
32										32

Continue the combination journal on the next page.

COMBINATION JOURNAL

PAGE 1 2 3 4

CASH		DATE	ACCOUNT TITLE	DOC. No.	POST. REF.	GENERAL	
DEBIT	CREDIT					DEBIT	CREDIT

GENERAL LEDGER

ACCOUNT _____ ACCOUNT NO. _____

DATE	ITEM	POST. REF.	DEBIT	CREDIT	BALANCE	
					DEBIT	CREDIT

ACCOUNT _____ ACCOUNT NO. _____

DATE	ITEM	POST. REF.	DEBIT	CREDIT	BALANCE	
					DEBIT	CREDIT

ACCOUNT _____ ACCOUNT NO. _____

DATE	ITEM	POST. REF.	DEBIT	CREDIT	BALANCE	
					DEBIT	CREDIT

ACCOUNT _____ ACCOUNT NO. _____

DATE	ITEM	POST. REF.	DEBIT	CREDIT	BALANCE DEBIT	CREDIT

ACCOUNT _____ ACCOUNT NO. _____

DATE	ITEM	POST. REF.	DEBIT	CREDIT	BALANCE DEBIT	CREDIT

ACCOUNT _____ ACCOUNT NO. _____

DATE	ITEM	POST. REF.	DEBIT	CREDIT	BALANCE DEBIT	CREDIT

ACCOUNT _____ ACCOUNT NO. _____

DATE	ITEM	POST. REF.	DEBIT	CREDIT	BALANCE DEBIT	CREDIT